THE MARRIAGE

Like the author's earlier Princess Ivona (published as
Playscript 13), The Marriage, written in 1946, is an impor-
tant forerunner of the Theatre of the Absurd. It is a play
about the shifting relationship between reality and imagination. Henry, a soldier stationed in northern France during
World War II, has a dream about his father, mother,'.
sweetheart and best friend; the dream constitutes the action
of the play. In the dream, Henry's imagination transforms
him and the other characters into players of multiple roles
- Father and King, Mother and Queen, Servant and Princess,
Son and Prince, Friend and Courtier. The author explores
the kind of transformations which occur in human relation-
ships and which allow a father to be elevated to kingship and
then deposed, the lost chastity of a young woman to be
restored by a respectable marriage and one's character
and relationship to others to be built totally through one's
individual perception. The Marriage provides a dramatic
exploration of the nature of absolute reality in relation to
the always changing reality of self and imagination.

The Marriage has received several major European productions. It was performed at the Theatre Recamier, Paris
in 1964 and at the Royal Dramatic Theatre, Stockholm in
1966. The author was born in Poland in 1904, settled in
France in 1963 and died there in 1969, having won the prestigious International Publishers Prize of $20,000 in 1967.
Apart from Princess Ivona, his two novels Pornografia
and Ferdydurke have also been published by Calder and
Boyars.

Louis Iribarne's translation is both fluent and sensitive to
the nuances of the original Polish.

PLAYSCRIPT 34

'the marriage'

witold gombrowicz

TRANSLATED BY LOUIS IRIBARNE

CALDER AND BOYARS · LONDON

First published in France 1953
in the Polish-language review 'Kultura'

ⓒ Witold Gombrowicz 1953

This translation first published in the United States of
America 1969 by Grove Press, Incorporated

ⓒ Grove Press, Incorporated 1969

This translation first published in Great Britain 1970
by Calder and Boyars Ltd
18 Brewer Street London W1R 4AS

ISBN 0 7145 0645 1 Cloth Edition
ISBN 0 7145 0646 X Paper Edition

Printed by photo-lithography
and made at the Pitman Press,
Bath.

ABOUT THE AUTHOR

WITOLD GOMBROWICZ was born in Poland in 1904 and studied law in Warsaw. His first work, a volume of short stories, was published in the revue Skamander and his novel, Ferdydurke, was published in 1937.

The outbreak of war found Gombrowicz in Argentina, where he stayed until 1963, not wishing to return to a communist dominated Poland. He continued to write but his work was hardly known outside Poland until the Polish emigre revue in Paris, Kultura, began to publish his work, Journals, and the two novels Pornografia and Cosmos.

With the 'thaw' in Poland, under Gomulka's comparatively liberal government, his books were published in Poland where they were received with great acclaim. Editions of 10,000 were exhausted within a few weeks and the government, amazed at the reaction to his work, banned Gombrowicz' books again.

Since then, however, Gombrowicz has attracted a wide public in Western Europe and his novel, Ferdydurke, has been translated into ten languages.

In 1963 he came to Europe to spend a year in Berlin at the invitation of theFord Foundation. He then settled in the South of France. In 1966 he won the prestigious International Publishers Prize. He died in 1969.

THE MARRIAGE has had several productions all over Europe. It was first produced by Jorge Lavelli at the Theatre Recamier in Paris in 1964 and since that date has been produced by Alf Sjoberg at the Royal Dramatic Theatre, Stockholm (in 1966) and also at the Schillertheater in West Berlin by Ernst Schroder. This translation was broadcast on BBC Radio 3 in 1969, directed by H. B. Fortuin.

Excerpt from an interview about THE MARRIAGE given by
Witold Gombrowicz in 1968

It was still wartime when I started work on THE MARRIAGE.
It gestated slowly, by fits and starts, during my time in the
Argentine: FAUST and HAMLET were my models, but only
because of their quality of genius. I wanted to write a play
which was 'great' and 'inspired', so I went back to those
works which in my youth I had read with veneration. And
my ambitions were not without a certain guile. I craftily
figured that to write a masterpiece was easier than writing
just an ordinarily good play. It seemed a lot less hard to
be a genius ...

Why was this? THE MARRIAGE, like all my works a revolt
against form, is a travesty of form, a parody of 'great
drama'. But if I was going to send up 'genius', couldn't I
also steal a little of it for myself? Who could tell whether I
had stolen it or not? ...

I wanted to show humanity on its way from the Church of
God to the Church of man. Yet I didn't start off with this
idea. At first, I started by throwing into the scene a hand-
ful of ideas, of images and situations and slowly, haltingly,
I evolved this main idea. When I'd come to the middle of
the second act, I still didn't know what I wanted. And the
stumbling creation of my MISSA SOLEMNIS which resem-
bled a drunk or sleepwalker or madman while rising out
of the short circuits of form, its connections and combin-
ations, its rhymes and interior rhythms, seemed similar
to the development of History, which also lurches forward
like a drunk or madman.

Then I wrote:

> " JOHNNY - No.
> HENRY - Nothing.
> THE FATHER - It's been transformed.
> THE MOTHER - Distorted.
> JOHNNY - Destroyed.
> HENRY - Dislocated. "

and I suddenly burst into tears like a child. Nothing like it had ever happened to me before - I was hysterical!

I wept bitterly, soaking the paper in front of me. It was not so much the fact that the words evoked my personal misfortunes that filled me with despair, but that they came so easily to me. I experienced their rhyme and rhythm like a sharp, stabbing pain. I wept with horror at the internal coherence of my misery. Then I stopped crying and I started to write.

D. R.   What happened to THE MARRIAGE?

W. G.   I translated it into Spanish with the help of my friend Alexander Roussowitch and thanks to the help of Cecilia Debenedetti and Stanislas Odyniec, it was published in Buenos Aires. The artistic circles of that capital ignored it. In 1963, Jorge Lavelli, a young Argentine director living in Paris, became interested in it. He mounted an excellent production at the Theatre Recamier, which was the starting point of his rapid rise to fame as a director. After a time, THE MARRIAGE found a great director in the shape of Alf Sjoberg, who did a production at the Royal Dramatic Theatre of Stockholm. Sjoberg put a lot of work and passion into the rehearsals of both THE MARRIAGE and PRINCESS IVONA and they were a great success. The third of the better productions of THE MARRIAGE took place at the Schillertheater in Berlin where there were fifty-one curtain calls at the preview. I owe a great deal to the director, Ernst Schroder, to his excellent company and in particular to Helmut Griem. Alas, through a set of unfortunate circumstances I didn't see one of these productions. To be honest, I haven't set foot in a theatre for thirty years. I write plays but I don't go to the theatre ... I don't know why ... Laziness, perhaps.

D. R.   How do you compare your plays with Beckett's or Ionesco's?

W. G.   I don't compare them. The critics do that. When PRINCESS IVONA and THE MARRIAGE were produced in Paris, they said they belonged to Beckett's and Ionesco's 'theatre of the absurd'. But PRINCESS IVONA was written in 1936, THE MARRIAGE in 1946, when no-one had heard of these writers. And also, my theatre isn't absurd.

Yes, THE MARRIAGE is obscure and dream-like and fantastical: because it is so full of shadows, I wouldn't know how to analyse it fully myself. I like the director to let this kind of sphinx evolve its own form freely - to cry out, to wander - so long as he is careful about the semi-musical harmony of the ceremonial. Nevertheless, THE MARRIAGE has an action which holds together and there is no reason for it not to be perceptible to the audience. You see, as I wanted these conversations to be a kind of clue to my works, I am going to tell you what THE MARRIAGE is about. Perhaps it will be useful to some director.

What THE MARRIAGE is about

THE MARRIAGE is a dream. A dream of Henry, a Polish soldier in the last war somewhere in France in the French army fighting the Germans. At the core of this dream are the anxieties of Henry for his family, lost down there at the bottom of Poland but also the most essential anxieties of contemporary man on the wrong side of two eras.

Surging into Henry's thoughts are his birthplace in Poland his parents, his fiancee Mary. The house is degraded, here it is turned into an inn. Mary has become Molly, a serving girl, a barmaid. The father is the barman.

The father is pursued by drunks. Then comes the key-scene: to defend his human dignity, the father shouts out that he is 'untouchable'.

'A king, a king, an untouchable king!' sneer the drunks.

And Henry pays homage to his father, who changes into a king. And not only does the father-king raise Henry to princely dignity, but he promises him as well a sacred and worthy marriage by means of his royal power, a marriage which will restore Molly, the barmaid, to her purity and integrity of yesteryear ...

The first act finishes there. It seems that human dignity is saved.

In the second act, preparations are made for this 'worthy and holy' marriage to be solemnised by a bishop. But doubts start to infiltrate into Henry's dream. This whole ceremony of marriage starts to wobble, as if threatened by Stupidity - as if he, Henry, striving with all his soul to be wise, dignified and pure, lacks confidence in himself and his dream ...

The chief drunk again bursts into the room, pissed as a newt! Henry is about to come to blows with him, when suddenly (as it happens in dreams) the scene changes into a reception at Court. The drunk is turned into the Ambassador of an enemy power, who incites Henry to treason.

'Betray your father the king", is more or less what the drunk says, 'the Bishop, King, Church and God are only old superstitions. Proclaim yourself king and then authority, divine or otherwise, will no longer be necessary to you, you will give yourself the sacrament of marriage and force everybody to recognise it and recognise Molly as pure and married to you. '

Such is the key to the metaphor of THE MARRIAGE, the transition from a world founded on divine and paternal authority to another where Henry's will becomes the divine, creative will ... like Hitler's or Stalin's.

Henry yields to the blandishments of the drunk. He dethrones his father and becomes king himself.

There follows a scene where the drunk asks Johnny, Henry's friend, to hold a flower over Molly's head: Johnny does so, the drunk pinches it, leaving Johnny and Molly in a compromising position, which no flower could justify. A terrible thought arises in Henry's mind that Molly ... and Johnny ...

'You pig!
You've bound them together
By a dreadful
And inferior bond.
You've married them
You pig priest!'

he screams.

End of Act Two.

In Act Three, Henry is dictator, who has tamed everybody, even his parents. The marriage preparations are gone through a second time, but this time without God or any sanction other than his absolute power.

Yet he feels that his power will have no meaning unless confirmed by someone making a voluntary sacrifice of his blood. That is why he urges Johnny to commit suicide for him. This sacrifice will appease his jealousy, make him strong and powerful enough to go through with the marriage ... and Molly's purity (and also to fulfil the dream ... all that he has been looking for since the start). Johnny agrees to this plan.

In the final scene, Johnny kills himself. But Henry weakens and recoils horrified at what he has done.

The marriage will not be fulfilled.

From an interview with Dominique de Roux
in Entretiens avec Gombrowicz,
Editions Piere Belford, 1968

Translated by Jonathan Hammond

THE MARRIAGE

THE MARRIAGE was first performed in January 1964, at the Theatre Recamier in Paris. The cast was as follows:

FRANK father and king	Alexis Nitzer
KATHARINE mother and queen	Juliette Brac
HENRY son and prince	Olivier Lebeaut
JOHNNY friend and courtier	Francois Mirante
MOLLY servant and princess	Claudine Raffalli
DRUNKARD	Fernand Berset
CHANCELLOR	Luc Delhumeau
CHAMBERLAIN)	
CHIEF OF POLICE)	Augy Hayter
BISHOP PANDULF)	
DIGNITARY / TRAITOR)	Andre Cazalas

The play was directed by Jorge Lavelli

This translation of THE MARRIAGE was broadcast on 21 March 1969, on BBC Radio 3. The cast was as follows:

FRANK	Maurice Denham
KATHARINE	Mary Morris
HENRY	Frank Finlay
JOHNNY	Christopher Guinee
MOLLY	Angela Pleasance
DRUNKARD	Felix Felton
CHANCELLOR	Lockwood West
CHAMBERLAIN	Frederick Treves
CHIEF OF POLICE	Francis de Wolff
BISHOP PANDULF	James Thomason
DIGNITARY / TRAITOR	Michael Deacon

The play was directed by H. B. Fortuin

ACT ONE

(An oppressive, forlorn landscape. In the shadows,
ruins of a disfigured church)

HENRY.

The curtain has risen ... An obscure church ...
An incongruous ceiling ... A strange vault ...
And the sign slips into the abyss of the abyss
Of the sphere of spheres, and stone and stone ...

Through an entrance that has never been entered
Stands a deformed altar of a foreign Psalter
Clasped shut by the absurdity of the chalice
That sinking into stillness gouges out the pastor ...

A void. A desert. Nothing, I am alone here
Alone
Alone

But perhaps I am not alone; who knows what is behind
me, perhaps ... something ... someone is standing
here alongside me, off to the side, off to the side,
some id ... some insuperable, ungovernable, idioti-
zed, idiotouchable idiot, who can touch and ... (With
alarm) I'd better not move ... no, don't move, because
if we move ... he'll move ... and touch ... (With
growing uneasiness) Oh, if only something or someone would come out from somewhere ... Aha! There's
something ...

(JOHNNY emerges from the shadows)

Johnny! It's Johnny!

JOHNNY. Henry!

HENRY.
> Imagine what a horrible dream I had
> I dreamt I saw some hideous monster, and
> I wanted to run, but couldn't!

JOHNNY.
> That stew they give us for supper is pretty
> Tough and indigestible. I have nightmares too
> Sometimes ...

HENRY. But at least you are of flesh and blood. Or perhaps you're only a dream too ... What are you doing
here, anyway?

JOHNNY. Don't ask me.

HENRY.
> Johnny, Johnny, why are you so frightfully sad?

JOHNNY.
> And you, why are you so sad?

HENRY.
> No special reason.

JOHNNY.
> No special reason.

HENRY. Something strange has happened to us. Where are
we? I'm afraid this place is under a curse ... and
we're under a curse too ... Excuse me if my words
sound artificial ... I'm unable to speak naturally ...

> A hundredfold sorrow
> A grief without cease or limit
> And a terrible oppression, dumb and dark,
> Have invaded my soul! Oh, God!
> Oh, God! Oh, God!

JOHNNY. (petulantly)
> What do you need God for when I am here?
> Don't you see, friend, that I am the same as you?
> Why let yourself get upset by ghosts

18

If you and I are of flesh and blood
If you are as I and I am as you!

HENRY. (joyously) "If you are as I and I am as you!" Oh,
what's the difference! But I'm very glad you're here,
Johnny! With you here it's a different story. But ...
Where are we? All the same I have the feeling ...
we're somewhere ... There ... there's something
over there ...

(Part of a wall becomes visible, some furniture, the
outline of a room)

I've seen all this before somewhere.

JOHNNY. So have I ...

HENRY. (dramatically)
We are somewhere
We are somewhere. But where?
What's that?

(A room appears - the dining room of a country manor
house in Poland that looks as though it has been transformed into a dive)

JOHNNY. (hesitantly) I swear this room reminds me of
something ... It reminds me a little of your dining
room in Maloszyce. It's similar and yet not similar
... That clock. That chest of drawers. There's the
room I slept in when I came to visit you during the
holidays ...

HENRY. Yes, but wait a minute - we're not in Maloszyce
... we're stationed at the front in northern France -
at the front in northern France - at the front in northern France. And if we're here, we can't be there!

JOHNNY. It's similar and yet not similar ... It would
seem to be the same dining room, even though it
does resemble a restaurant or a dive ... or an inn ...
or a boardinghouse ... or a tavern ...

19

HENRY. This room is disguised and everything is abnormal.

JOHNNY.
>Don't be silly, stop trying to complicate matters.
>What do you care if something's abnormal
>As long as we are normal!
>And these chairs are real, they're made of wood,
>and one is sure to find something in the cupboard.
>But why isn't anyone here? Hallo!

HENRY. (terrified) Don't shout! Wait! You'd better not shout!

JOHNNY.
>Why shouldn't I shout?
>Hallo! Is anybody here? Is everybody dead? Hallo!

HENRY.
>Fool! Shut your trap!
>Shhh! Be quiet, I say! Hallo!
>Why doesn't anybody come out? Shhh! Hallo!

JOHNNY. Hallo!

HENRY. Hallo!

JOHNNY. Hallo!

(Enter the FATHER, old, rigid, sclerotic, distrustful ...)

HENRY. At last, someone ... Excuse me, is this a restaurant? (Silence) Is this a restaurant?

FATHER. And what if it is?

HENRY. (in the style of a traveller)
>Tell me, is it possible
>To get a bite to eat here?

FATHER. (in the style of an innkeeper)
>I suppose so
>But by shouting you won't get anywhere

20

HENRY. (to JOHNNY) That voice sounds familiar.

JOHNNY. He looks very similar to your father ... I swear
    it's him, though on second thoughts ... I'm not so
    sure ... It's hard to tell at first sight.

HENRY. You're crazy. If that were my father, he'd be
    the first to recognize us. No, come on, let's forget
    about it. That's not my father. Come on, let's sit
    down. (To the FATHER) Is this an inn? I mean, is it
    possible to get a room for the night here?

FATHER. (grudgingly) I suppose so, seeing as how we
    rent rooms here. But you better watch your p's and
    q's!

HENRY.
    Watch my p's and q's ...

FATHER. (crescendo)
    Be polite and respectful!

HENRY.
    Oh, I see, respectful ...

FATHER. (shouting)
    Civil and courteous!

(Enter the MOTHER, an elderly woman, worn out,
dressed in rags. She joins in shouting with the FATHER)

MOTHER. You'd better behave yourselves, and mind you
    no hanky-panky, because we won't hold with that
    around here ... we'll have no part in that, thank you
    very much ...

JOHNNY. (to HENRY) That's your mother.

HENRY. (loudly)
    It would seem so
    But it's not altogether certain
    This is all a little confusing, but I shall
    Straighten everything out!

21

(To JOHNNY) Forgive me for speaking artificially,
but I feel as though I were in an artificial situation.
(Raises the lamp)

Come over here
Come over here ... Come over here, I say

Come closer, that's it, closer! I swear, you'd think
I were trying to lure a bunch ... a bunch of chickens
... Keep coming! Closer! Look how grudgingly they
come. Come a little closer or else I shall have to
come closer.

I'll come closer, and as I come closer

You come closer ... My God, it's as though I were
trying to catch a bunch of fish. But why is it so quiet
around here?

My father has stepped out of the shadows
But he's changed so much
I can hardly recognize him
And moreover so strangely silent that
I must speak the whole time alone
Alone must I speak until I'm transformed
Into a priest of my father!
And here comes my mother like a steamer
To tell the truth she's not very similar to my
    mother
Perhaps I should just drop the matter. How strange
My voice sounds. Let's leave them alone since
They wish to be left alone.

JOHNNY. Maybe they're not your parents at all.

HENRY.
It's them all right, I know perfectly well it's them
But something's happened to them and for some
    reason
They're pretending not to be them
Perhaps they've gone crazy ...

JOHNNY. Try talking to them in a straightforward manner
    Henry.

22

HENRY.
   ... And I'm unable to speak to them straightfor-
      wardly, because
   There's something very solemn and mysterious
      about all this
   Exactly as though a mass were being celebrated!
   I feel like laughing when I see how solemn I've
      become!
   My words sound so dignified! I simply amused
   To see how grave and solemn I've become
   But at the very same time I tremble and trembling
      I declare
   That I tremble - and as a result of this declaration
   I tremble even harder and trembling even harder

   I again declare that I tremble even harder ... But to
   whom do I make this declaration? To whom? Someone
   is listening to me ...

   But I don't know who - and as a matter of fact
   I am alone here, all alone, since you are not here
   No! There's no one else here! I am alone
   All alone, completely alone... Oh, weep! Yes, shed
   Tears for me, because I am alone, alone, alone!

JOHNNY.   Don't say that ... Why do you say such things?

HENRY.   Still, if they are my parents the least I could do
   is go up to them and say hello ...

   Father! Mother!
   Papa! Mamma! It's me, Henry!
   I've come home from the war!

FATHER.   (reluctantly)
   Mother ... it's Henry!

MOTHER.
   Henry! Good Heavens!

HENRY.   (with animation)
   Hey, they said something!

MOTHER. Oh, who could have ever foreseen by a divine
premonition that something like this ... oh, my little
treasure, my little sunshine, my little sweet pea,
oh, how could I have been so blind, and how I used to
cry my eyes out for fear I would never see you again,
my little sunshine, but here you are, my little sweet
pea, my little sparrow, my little treasure, oh, and
how you've grown, you're a man now, alleluia,
alleluia, come here, let me hug you, my little sweet
pea, my little sparrow, my little treasure, my little
sunshine, oh, oh, oh ...

HENRY.
Come, let's hug each other.

MOTHER.
Oh, yes, yes, let's hug each other.

FATHER.
Well, all right, let's hug each other.

MOTHER.
Come, let me hug you.

FATHER. Wait a minute! Not like that.

HENRY. But it's only mamma!

FATHER. Mamma or no mamma, I wouldn't get too close
if I were you.

HENRY. But ... but I am the son.

FATHER. Son or no son, I wouldn't get too close if I were
you. ... Maybe you are the son, but there's no telling
what the son has been up to all these years. No sooner
does he set foot inside the door and right away he has
to be hugged. (Sharply) Well, nobody's going to put
his arms around me, see, 'cos I'm not an old sack
you can just dump in any corner you like!

HENRY. (To JOHNNY) They've gone crazy.

JOHNNY. (to HENRY) They've gone crazy.

FATHER. And you can cut out all this matey business too,
     'cos once you start that the next thing you know is some
     bastard'll up and pull a fast one on you and then,
     whaam, right in the kisser ... or somewhere else
     for all I know ... and then pretty soon they'll be
     trying to take advantage of you, pushing you about and
     knocking you in the chops, persecuting the hell out of
     you, hounding and tormenting you, with no regard
     whatsoever for age or sex, with their bloody, pitiless,
     spiteful spite ...

HENRY. They've gone crazy.

JOHNNY. They've gone crazy.

HENRY. (unrestrainedly, emphatically, theatrically)
     It's obvious they couldn't take it
     They've lost their wits
     After all these long and agonizing years
     But such is life. The world nowadays is swarming
     With half-wits ...

JOHNNY. (as above)
     The world is swarming with half-wits. At least
     Half of all the mothers and fathers in the world
     Have lost their wits because they couldn't endure
     Suffering, affliction and disease
     I know of many such cases myself.

HENRY.
     So do I!

     (Falls silent, ashamed) Nevertheless, I must try to
     make a little conversation with them. (Loudly, in a
     conventional tone) To tell the truth, I didn't recognize
     you at first.

MOTHER. Neither did we.

HENRY. I didn't recognize you, because ... well, because
     I didn't expect ... But that doesn't matter. It's not

of any real importance. So how have you been getting
along?

FATHER. Not bad. What about you?

HENRY. All right, I suppose.

FATHER. Hm ...

HENRY. Hm ...

(Silence)

Well, what'll we do now? We can't just stand here
and do nothing ...

FATHER. Nothing.

MOTHER. Nothing.

HENRY. Nothing.

JOHNNY. (unexpectedly) I could eat something.

MOTHER. But of course! Here we are jabbering away
about nothing, oh, but of course, what's the matter
with me, of course, one has to have a bite to eat,
certainly, just a minute ... I'll have something ready
in less than no time, why of course, this is a day
to celebrate, because our darling Henry has come
home, let's see, we'll find something to eat, just a
minute, just a minute ... Here's a table and here are
a few chairs ... You'll have to settle for potluck, it
isn't what you'd call a feast exactly, but it'll have to
do, I suppose, alleluia, alleluia ...

FATHER. That's the spirit, mother, fix us something to
eat, but in a manner which is fitting, with respect ...
as is proper ... And so, in the name of the Father
and of the Son, of the Mother and of the Son, please
be seated at our table, my son ... But we can't just
sit down at the table in any old way ... The table's
over there and we're over here .. so give me your arm

26

my son, and you, old girl, let this young gentleman
show you to the table, for such is how it has always
been in our family for centuries and centuries, amen.
And now, forward, march!

HENRY. Very well.

(They walk two by two)

MOTHER.
I still can remember how His Reverence the Pastor
Escorted me to all the festivities at Easter
The table would be laid, the guests all engaged
In the most cheerful conversation!

FATHER. (thunderously)
In those days, gentlemen, a man would sit down
To a freshly laid table, and tuck away his pea soup
With such appetite and zest, one would have thought
He were ringing the bells or blowing a trombone!

JOHNNY.
How pleasant it is to walk and how pleasant
To exclaim words out loud!
But if we all continue to prate
I'm afraid we shall never get anything to eat!

HENRY.
I'm a little confused about this procession of ours.
  I'm not sure
Whether I am leading father, or he is leading me
And the form of our meeting strikes me as queer
But one must adapt oneself to the general atmos-
    phere....

ALL.
Yes, each must adapt himself to the general atmos-
    phere!
Each must adapt himself to the other! Then a con-
    cert will erupt!

HENRY. How extraordinary!

(They sit down at the table).

MOTHER. Forgive us for offering you such a modest meal,
Henry, and you too, Johnny ... but you see, we do
the best we can under the circumstances. This is a
soup made from horse guts and cat piss.

FATHER. Be quiet, woman! What difference does it make
what it's made from. You've probably noticed, Henry,
that you've found us in a somewhat embarrassing situation in this dumpy, dumpable dump of a roadside
dump - well, you see, that's because there was a
storm, a snowstorm, the roads were closed, not a
soul, thunder and lightning, puddles of water, mud
everywhere ... Keep your spoon where it is, son,
your father hasn't lifted his spoon to his mouth yet.

HENRY. This tavern ... it reminds me of something.

FATHER. Never mind about that, forget about it.

MOTHER. There isn't any.

JOHNNY. No.

HENRY. Nothing.

FATHER. It's been transformed.

MOTHER. Distorted.

JOHNNY. Destroyed.

HENRY. Dislocated.

All right, all right, they have gone crazy. But they
couldn't have gone crazy, because they don't exist
and I am only dreaming ... and the surest sign they
don't exist is that I'm able to say they don't exist
right in front of them. They only exist in my head. Oh,
my head! I've been talking to myself the whole time!

JOHNNY. How's that? What do you mean you've been
talking to yourself the whole time?

HENRY. Oh, skip it! (He begins to eat)

FATHER. Keep your spoon where it is - your father still hasn't lifted his to his mouth yet.

HENRY. Father, mother - how oppressive all these dreams are - father, mother - as if I didn't have enough problems of my own - father, mother - and all this time I thought they were dead - but not only are they not dead, they are sitting here and ...

FATHER. You are a faithful and devoted son, and consequently you will not wish to commence eating before he who has sired you ...

HENRY. And I won't go back to my family. I don't have a family any more. I am no longer a son.

FATHER. (as though he were preaching a sermon) Gone forever is that love and fidelity which the son has always owed the father, because for centuries and centuries, amen, the father has always been a hallowed and sacrosanct saint, an object of filial devotion under the pain of eternal chastisement ...

HENRY. I am a son of the war!

FATHER. And whoever raised a sacrilegious hand against his father would commit a crime so appalling, so unnatural, so abominable, so monstrous that afterwards he would pass the rest of his days, from one generation to the next, amid screams and groans of anguish, as one condemned by God and by Nature, heaped with shame, abandoned, accursed, rejected, forsaken, tormented ...

HENRY. The old man's afraid I might belt him ...

FATHER. Good soup.

HENRY. (to JOHNNY) Think you could beat the daylights out of this father?

JOHNNY. If you could, I could.

29

FATHER. Pass me the salt.

HENRY. And you wouldn't feel any pangs of conscience afterwards?

JOHNNY. I would if I were alone, but not if there were the two of us, because one would imitate the other.

FATHER. Nothing I like better than stuffing myself with tripe.

HENRY. (to JOHNNY) Ha, ha, ha! Well said, Johnny, well said. I agree with what you said just now - ha, ha, ha, yes, yes, I agree with you one hundred per cent. But that's beside the point. (With growing anxiety) No, that's completely beside the point. That's not what I had in mind at all. Oh, the hell with it! I'll be damned if I know what's going on around here! All I know is that this is all frightfully oppressive, because everything is twisted, understand, bunged up, plugged up, yes, that's it, plugged up ... and disguised ... but it seems as if we're not the only ones here ... I would like to penetrate, elucidate, to solve the riddle ... (He turns the lamp into the centre of the room, revealing MOLLY, who is asleep in a chair) Who is that girl?

MOTHER. Oh, that's the girl who does the service around here.

HENRY. Service?

MOTHER. That's right, a maidservant ... she serves as a maid.... Molly, bring us those scraps and that cat cutlet that are lying on the window sill ...

(The FATHER scratches himself)

Are you itching again?

HENRY. By the way, as long as we're going on about nothing in particular ... Are any of our friends still alive?

FATHER. A few.

HENRY. Tell me something, I'd be curious to know ...
whatever became of Mary, you remember, the girl I
was once engaged to ... the one who used to come
here for the holidays....

FATHER. I don't see any cutlet.

MOTHER. Maybe somebody swiped it.

MOLLY. (comes closer) It's not on the window.

MOTHER. Go and look in the reception room, but no
dilly-dallying, mind you ... Clear the dishes away
first.

HENRY. What's your name?

MOLLY. Molly.

FATHER. (in an ambiguous tone) Molly.

MOTHER. (as above) Molly.

FATHER.
        She's a servant girl ... She serves ...

MOTHER.
        We hired her ... for everything ...

FATHER.
        She's an all-round servant.

MOTHER.
        She serves the guests.

FATHER.
        She serves to render service ...
        Molly

MOTHER. Molly ...

FATHER. Molly ...

HENRY. (to JOHNNY, quietly, sadly) What do you think about all this?

JOHNNY. (quietly, helplessly) I don't know ... I don't know ...

HENRY. (to JOHNNY) No, but I know!

JOHNNY. (to HENRY) If that's her, why doesn't she speak up? ... She couldn't have forgotten us ... Say something to her, Henry.

HENRY.
No.
How can I speak to her if
She no longer exists
She used to exist ...
Oh, what a dirty trick!
I once had a noble father and mother
And a fiancee as well, but now it appears
My father has shut himself up in some inexplicable tower
My mother has become equivocal
And my fiancee has been swallowed up by a slut
Bunged, beaten and plugged up by a slut
And forever imprisoned in a slut ...
Oh, what a dirty trick!
How vile! How base! How vulgar! But the worst thing of all is
I couldn't give a damn ... Hear
With what ease I say that: I couldn't give a damn.

JOHNNY. (lightly) Neither could I.

HENRY. (lightly)
To tell the truth,
I don't have the faintest idea
How I should behave:
The girl I was once engaged to has now become a slut.

JOHNNY. What of it?

32

HENRY.
        What of it?
        Exactly - what of it - since
        All of this is just a mere detail.

JOHNNY.
        A detail!
        Millions of girls
        Have suffered the same fate.

HENRY.
        Exactly!
        Millions of other people
        Are in the same situation as I.

JOHNNY. The world over!

HENRY. In Warsaw and Peking!

JOHNNY. In Verona and Barcelona!

HENRY. In Paris and in Venice!

JOHNNY. In Liverpool and Istanbul!

MOTHER. In Lyons and in Toulons!

FATHER. In Bucharest and Budapest!

JOHNNY. In Dublin and Berlin!

HENRY. Come on, let's dance!

ALL. (suddenly) Let's dance!

HENRY.
        The son has returned to the house of his parents
        But the house is no longer the house
        And the son is no longer the son. So who
        Has returned and to what?
        Let's forget about the past! Let's march forward!
        May no one return to anything!

(Quiet)

Here is where I sat with her, and once again I'm
sitting here. But what difference does it make? It's
all over now. Finished. There's something else now
and there'll be something else again tomorrow. It's
not worth repeating.

(Quiet)

JOHNNY. It's not worth repeating!

HENRY. (in a romantic tone)
        Do you see this chair here? That's where I sat
          with her
        On that memorable night! This is where
        My mother sat and my father over there!
        Exactly as I'm sitting here now. Do you remember?
        That memorable night, our last night together?

MOTHER. Of course I do, my child, of course I remember
        ... I sat right over here, and we had sour milk for
        supper ...

FATHER. I sat over here.

JOHNNY. And I sat here ... here, in this chair, because
        I remember I was looking out of the window and I
        said: "There are flies here." It all comes back to me
        now!

HENRY. And I sat over here ... (He sits down) I was
        buttering my bread, with her beside me here ... I
        was buttering my bread. (To JOHNNY) Why don't you
        sit down? Sit down. I was buttering my bread.

        And I said: Schearing
        Has inquired about that syringe again.

FATHER. I said something, but I can't remember what.

MOTHER. You don't have a very good memory, but I do
        ... Now what was it you said? Oh, yes! You said,

34

"My sleeve," ... nothing else, just "my sleeve,"
because he'd just got his sleeve caught against the
salad dish.

FATHER. That's it! That's it! That's it! I said, "My
sleeve," on my word of honour! What an extraordinary
memory you have!

HENRY. And then I started drumming my fingers on the
table and I said: "I'm getting married in three months."

MOTHER. That's just what he said, my little sparrow,
that's exactly what he said, those are the exact same
words he used, that's just how he put it. And then I
laid down my cup, chased away another fly and said:
"Henry, what's the matter with you? What's that
you're saying? Are you engaged? But isn't that a
little ..." No, I've got it all wrong. First I said:
"Henry, darling, what are you saying? ... Pass me
the sugar."

FATHER. That's right, that's right, and then I said "Let
them be happy, mother! Now, now, no need to cry.
Bring us something to drink! You're both a little
young, but never mind that." You should have seen
her blush! Turned red as a tomato! Well, I never! Ha,
ha, ha!

MOTHER. And then she said something.

HENRY.
       Yes, she said something, but she's gone now.
       The wedding fell through. Finished. Nothing.
       There she is, hiding in the closet! She refuses to
          come out.
       Oh, what's the use! I'm surrounded by a void. And
          all she does is pout.
       Forward! Forward!

ALL. (except MOLLY) Forward!

FATHER. The hell with it, dammit!

HENRY. (to JOHNNY) How do you like that - a common ordinary maidservant!

JOHNNY. Well, so what if she's a maidservant?

HENRY. That's right, so what if she's a maidservant.

JOHNNY. She's not even bad-looking.

HENRY. You're right, she's not bad-looking, at that.

JOHNNY. Does she sleep here?

HENRY. Does she sleep here?

JOHNNY. (playfully) I would like some tea. (To MOLLY) Psssst ... Psssst ...

FATHER. What's all this psssst-psssst for? There's no need to psssst around here. If you want something else, all you have to do is ask me. And don't think you can get away with anything, 'cos we're not running some dive here, you know ... Ohoh, did you see that? They're already givin' her the eye! Christ Almighty, it's always the same, night or day, some-one's trying to pinch her, pat her, cuddle her, fondle her, tickle her crotch, and it always winds up in trouble, trouble, trouble ... (Sharply) Don't try to cause any trouble, I'm warning you fellers!

MOTHER. (in a shrill voice) Frankie!

FATHER. Don't start anything, I'm warning you!

MOTHER. Calm down, Frankie!

FATHER. Kindly keep your piggish paws off this swinish sow of a pigged-up pig of a swineherder's pig prick!

MOTHER. Look at him slobber!

FATHER. Pig, pig, pig!

(The DRUNKARD staggers in)

DRUNKARD. Porky Molly!

FATHER. Get out of here!

DRUNKARD. Hey, Molly, how about a little piece of pork,
    eh?

FATHER. I'll get it for you myself.

HENRY. (on the other side, amused) Porky Molly!

FATHER. (running up to him) I'll serve it to him!

DRUNKARD. Hey, Molly, give me some pork!

HENRY. (obstinately)
    Porky Molly!

DRUNKARD.
    Give me some pork, Molly!

HENRY.
    Porky Molly!

FATHER.
    Oh, for Christ's sake!

DRUNKARD.
    Pig!

HENRY. (yelling into space)
    Pig!

JOHNNY.
    Pig!

MOTHER. (aside)
    Heaven help us - what a pig!

FATHER. (to the DRUNKARD)
    Get out of here!

DRUNKARD.
A bottle of bitters!

FATHER. (to HENRY)
Get out of here!

HENRY.
A bottle of bitters!

DRUNKARD. (louder)
A bottle of bitters!

HENRY. (louder)
A bottle of bitters!

FATHER.
Good God!

DRUNKARD.
A bottle of pig bitters!

HENRY. A bottle of pig bitters!

JOHNNY. A bottle of pig bitters!

(The DRUNKARDS come in)

DRUNKARDS.
Chug, chug, chug!

FATHER.
Gentlemen, be reasonable!
It's almost closing time. Molly, lock the doors!

(The DRUNKARDS sit down at the table)

DRUNKARDS.
Some stout!
A pint!
Some brawn!
A double shot, straight!
Molly, some stout! Molly, some kielbasa! Molly,
some sausage!

38

Molly, some brawn!

HENRY. (aside)
Molly, some brawn!

DRUNKARDS.
Maxie's an ice-cream man
Hits the bottle when he can
Chug, chug, chug!

FATHER. (to MOLLY) Hey ... don't wait on that table!

DRUNKARD. Ah, come on, Molly, come on over here for
a second, I want to tell you something, Molly me
darling ...

FATHER. Don't go Molly.

DRUNKARD. Aaah, shut your bloody trap, grandpa ... If
I feel like calling the waitress she's no right to refuse,
damn it, and if you try and get tough with me, you
old duffer, I'll blow myself up and blow off your
crucifix!

HENRY. (aside) Blow off his crucifix!

FATHER. Wait a minute, wait a minute! Okay, okay - Molly,
go and wait on that table!

DRUNKARD. (looking at him)
He's got the shits.

DRUNKARDS. (matter-of-factly)
He's got the shits.

HENRY. (aside)
He's got the shits.

DRUNKARD.
Shuuut up ...
Close ranks! March!
Forward! Let's go!

(A furious march)

DRUNKARDS.
>   Maxie's an ice-cream man
>   Hits the bottle when he can
>   Chug, chug, chug!

(They stop in front of the FATHER)

DRUNKARD.
>   Shut your traaap ... you pig ...
>   Pig!
>   He's got the shits ...
>   That's what's the matter, he's got a bad case of
>   the shits
>   He's gone and dirtied his pants!

2nd DRUNKARD. (gloomily)
>   He's got the shits.

3rd DRUNKARD.
>   Has he ever ...

DRUNKARD. And seeing as how I've scared the shit out
of him, I'm going to let him have it. Isn't that so,
Miss Molly?

DRUNKARDS.
>   Well, let 'im have it then! Let 'im have it!

DRUNKARD.
>   I'm going to let 'im have it!

DRUNKARDS.
>   Well, let 'im have it then! Let 'im have it!

DRUNKARD.
>   I'm going to let 'im have it!

HENRY.
>   Well, let 'im have it!

DRUNKARD.
>   I'm going to let 'im have it!

MOTHER. (in a shrill voice) Frankie, they're going to let

40

you have it!

DRUNKARDS.
All right, boys, let's let 'im have it!

DRUNKARD.
All right, let's let 'im have it!

(They advance towards the FATHER)

DRUNKARDS.
All right, let 'im have it!

DRUNKARD.
I'm going to let 'im have it!

(Silence)

I'd let him have it, but the bastardly bastard has
a kisser like a rock ...
It won't budge ... And if it won't budge, then ...
(To MOLLY) Molly!
There's a lot of room on the floor!

DRUNKARDS. (sullenly) It won't budge ... (To MOLLY)
Molly ...

DRUNKARD. And that's not all ... Look how quiet it's
become ...

HENRY. (to himself, aloud) It's true. It has become quiet
in here ...

DRUNKARD. Chug, chug, chug!

(A furious march)

DRUNKARDS.
Maxie's an ice-cream man
He hits the bottle when he can
Chug, chug, chug!

Well, let 'im have it!

41

DRUNKARD.
Okay, I'm going to let 'im have it!

HENRY. (to himself) How much longer can this go on?

DRUNKARD. (aside, in a different tone) Not much longer now.

HENRY. (to the DRUNKARD) What's outside the window?

DRUNKARD. (as above) Fields - as far as the eye can see.

(The DRUNKARDS approach the FATHER)

But first of all I'm going to smash this guy right in the kisser and then I'm going to stamp all over him, flatten him, squish out his guts and spit all over him 'cos I'm not afraid - Molly ...

But he's got a mug like a rock!
And if it won't budge, there's not a damn thing I can do ...
But what a mug he's got, what a mug!

2nd DRUNKARD.
A mug like a house!

3rd DRUNKARD.
A mug like a priest!

(Silence)

4th DRUNKARD. (suddenly) Hey, he's got a fly on his nose!

DRUNKARD. So what?

4th DRUNKARD. Well, why don't you knock it off for him? You're not going to just let it sit there, are you? Isn't that right, Miss Molly?

DRUNKARD. Bloodybloodybloody fly, bloodybloodybloody fly, bloodybloodybloody fly ... (He raises his hand)

42

FATHER. (very softly) Don't you dare ...

HENRY. (aside, dramatically) Oh, oh, he said something!

FATHER. (softly)
    Don't you dare, I won't tolerate it
    I won't tolerate it
    I won't stand for it
    I won't stand for it, because I won't stand for it
    I can't stand it!
    And if I can't stand it, then ... then ...
    Then I don't know what ...

DRUNKARD. (confidentially)
    I'm going to let 'im have it, Molly, I'm going to
    let 'im have it!

DRUNKARDS. (confidentially)
    Well, let 'im have it then, let 'im have it!

FATHER. (shouting)
    You pigs!
    Keep away from me, or you'll be sorry
    If anybody touches me, something awful
    I repeat: something awful
    So awful that ... that I don't know what.
    There'll be weeping and screaming and the gnash-
      ing of teeth,
    The rack and execution, hell and execration,
    A levelling, piercing, pulverizing squeal
    That'll blow this whole universe to kingdom come
    ... Indeed! Indeed!

    Because no one, because no one may touch me
    Because no one, because no, be-be-because
    I'm untouchable, I'm untouchable, I'm untouchable
    Because I'll curse the lot of you!

DRUNKARDS.
    Tut, tut, tut! A king, a king, an untouchable king!

DRUNKARD.
    Get a load of him! He's a king!

Just for that I'm going to touch him with this finger!
Isn't that right, Miss Molly?

FATHER. (fleeing) Keep away from me, or I'll curse you!

HENRY. (suddenly) Stop! Stay where you are!

(The stage becomes motionless)

I really don't know how I ought to behave ... (To
JOHNNY) Johnny! But I suppose I shall have to behave
somehow or other ... (With regret) Forgive me for
speaking in an artificial manner, but everything here
is artificial!

JOHNNY. (briskly, defiantly)
Don't worry about it!
What do you care if something is artificial
As long as you yourself are natural!

HENRY.
That's right, I am natural, I would like to be nat-
ural
I don't want to be solemn! But how can I help
Not being solemn when my voice sounds solemn?

(Silence)

What a terrifying silence.
It's so quiet my ears are ringing
And how strange, how awfully
Strange that I am speaking
But if I were silent
My silence would likewise seem strange
What am I to do?
Suppose I sat down
In this chair here
(He sits down)
  and started
Cracking jokes, laughing, or moving
My hands and feet ... No, it's no use! Even
The artlessness of these gestures is artificial
And they are transformed into some sort of spell ...

44

Suppose I put my feet up on this table, tossed back my
head, lit a cigarette and said: What business is it of
mine whether they beat up my father or rape my ex-
fiancee? ... What's the sense of blowing everything
out of proportion?

  Let's not exaggerate!

What's one more or less ... Can't he stand it? But I
can stand it that he can't stand it ... Father, father
...

  What kind of a father is he anyway? He's an ord-
    inary father
  The most ordinary kind of father ... We are all
  The most ordinary kind of people ... Suppose I
    say
  All this and even more. Very well. I said it
  But this again
  Sounds solemn, and transforms what I am saying
    into a
  DECLARATION
  And it sinks like a stone
  Into that silence ... Aha! Now I know why
  I do not speak but declare. Because you are not here
  And I am alone, alone, alone. I am not speaking
  To anyone and therefore I must be artificial
  Because if I am not speaking to anyone and yet I
    speak just the same
  Then I must be artificial.

What'll I do? Sit down? No. Go for a walk? That doesn't
make any sense either. But I can't go on behaving as
though I had nothing to do with all this. What's a
person supposed to do in such a situation? I might
kneel down, that's true, I might kneel down ...
Of course that would be pretty ... but I did say I
might kneel down ... even though it would look a
little ... but I did say I might kneel down ...

(He kneels down a little on one side)

Well, what do you know! I knelt down. But I knelt

down quietly and not for myself, but for them, and
not for them, but for myself as though I were a
priest ... a priest ... of what I don't know ...

FATHER. (abruptly, aside) Of what I don't know.

MOTHER. Nobody knows.

DRUNKARD. There's nobody here.

JOHNNY. Nobody, nothing.

HENRY.
      It doesn't matter!
      I am kneeling here before him! And now try
      To dismiss my genuflection, now try to
      Ignore my genuflection, now try to make it
      Disappear! (To the DRUNKARD) Go on, hit him!
      I kneel down before him!

2nd DRUNKARD. The King!

MOTHER. The King!

DRUNKARD. The King!

DRUNKARDS. The King! The King!

HENRY. What do you mean, the King?

DRUNKARDS. (completely drunk)
      The King, the King, the King!

(Their cries become more and more accelerated in
tempo. The DIGNITARIES come in)

FATHER.
      Henry!
      Oh, oh, Henry!

MOTHER.
      Oh, Henry!

DIGNITARIES.
　　Henry!

HENRY.
　　Oh, Henry! (Stands up)

FATHER.
　　Thank you, my son, I accept the homage which
　　　you have rendered me
　　I accept it and once again I accept it
　　And I cannot accept it enough ...
　　(With sincerity) Long have I thirsted after honours.

HENRY. What kind of a masquerade is this?

　　(Quiet)

FATHER. (with difficulty, vehemently)
　　Dignitaries!

DIGNITARIES.
　　The King! The King!

FATHER.
　　Dignitaries of my Person!

DIGNITARIES.
　　The King! The King!

FATHER.
　　Dignitaries of my dignity! Bid welcome to the Prince
　　Bow down before him in humble obeisance,
　　Prince Henry, my son, who from a far-off war
　　Has come.

HENRY. What kind of rubbish is this?

FATHER. (gravely, sclerotically)
　　Help! Help!

　　Oh, sweet Jesus of Nazareth! Oh, Mary most holy!
　　Oh, Jesus, my Jesus! Help me! But it was he, my
　　son, my seed, my offspring most holy who only a

moment ago delivered me from

> This sow of a souse who, in his drunken stupor,
> Blindly, brazenly, with extreme wantonness,
> Rushed at me and with
> His
> Piggish
> Finger

My untouchable person tried to touch! My person!
My person! My untouch ... Nobody may touch ...
because it's forbidden ... Prohibited. Nobody!

DIGNITARIES. Oh, sweet Jesus!

FATHER.
> He won't try to touch me any more!
> Nor inflate himself to deflate my person
> Nor squish, nor stamp, nor spit on me!
> Because Henry, Henry, Henry! Oh, Henry!

MOTHER. (triumphantly)
> Henry!

DIGNITARIES.
> Oh, Henry!

HENRY.
> Oh, Henry!
> This is getting sillier by the minute!

FATHER.
> Kneel down
> Kneel down, Henry!

HENRY. What for?

MOTHER. (in a shrill voice) Kneel down, Henry!

FATHER.
> Kneel down, kneel down! I'll kneel down too
> Kneel down! Let everyone kneel ... (He kneels)

(The DIGNITARIES kneel down)

HENRY. I'm not going to stand here by myself ... (He
gazes around with distrust and kneels down) I wish
to hell I knew what was going on. (He notices that he
and his FATHER are kneeling opposite one another)
I am kneeling before him and he is kneeling before me.
This is a farce! What an old copycat he is! (With
increasing rage) How disgusting!

FATHER. Wait a minute! I'm kneeling in the wrong dir-
ection. (Kneels down with his back to HENRY) I
kneel down before the Lord! I address myself to
the Lord! I commend myself to Almighty God, to the
Holy Trinity, to His inexhaustible goodness, to His
mercy most holy, His protection most sublime ...
Oh, Henry, Henry! ... In Him is there shelter, in
Him is there comfort, in Him is our refuge ...

        My Father
        Thy son am I
        Thou art my Father ...

HENRY. He's praying.

FATHER.
        Thou art my king!

HENRY. I can't get up now - it wouldn't be proper.

FATHER.
        Oh, my Father, Oh, my King, to Thee I do
            solemnly swear
        Love
        Honour
        Respect

HENRY. He's swearing to God, but it's as if I were
swearing to him. (Aloud) I've had about all I can
take of this. (Stands up)

FATHER. Henry, Henry ... My Father, I stand beside
Thee, I am Thy servant. I shall not forsake Thee,

my Father, and in return Thou shalt ... Thou shalt
return my beloved to me, my sweetheart, amen, amen,
amen ... so that everything may be done in a respectable manner, as is fitting ...

HENRY. Hey, what is this? Is he whispering to God or to
me?

FATHER.
Thou shalt return my betrothed to me!

HENRY. He will return my betrothed to me?

FATHER.
Thou shalt grant me a marriage!

HENRY. He will grant me a marriage?

FATHER. Thou shalt grant me a respectable marriage ...
a proper marriage as has always been the custom
in our family ... As it was in former times! Let
everything be as it used to be! Thou shalt grant me a
marriage to this chaste and immaculate virgin, my
fiancee, my sweetheart ... a respectable marriage
...

(Everyone slowly rises)

HENRY. A marriage?

FATHER. A marriage.

MOTHER. A marriage.

HENRY. A marriage?

FATHER. A marriage.

MOLLY. A marriage.

A DIGNITARY. A marriage.

MOTHER. A marriage.

A DIGNITARY. A marriage.

HENRY. A marriage?

(The FATHER and MOTHER smile at him indulgently, with delight, with emotion)

FATHER.
In the name of the Father
And of the Son! Do you see
This young lady here who in appearance
Is nothing but an ordinary maidservant?
The maidservant of some dumpy dump?

DIGNITARIES. We see her, Sire.

FATHER. (emphatically, insistently)
This girl is neither a whore
Nor a maidservant! She is a noble,
Modest, untouchable young lady who has been
Ravished, enslaved, tortured, plugged up,
Abused and spat upon by these good-for-nothing
bums ...
In defiance of all laws, human and divine ... Damn
you pigs!
This girl is not a pig! Have
A little heart, you people! A little understanding!
Have a little pity! Therefore I do declare
And I decree, I command with all my might, I
declare once and for all,
To all those present
That I restore her former dignity
And command that she be honoured
As though she were myself or the Most Holy
Virgin in her untouchable honour, in the name
Of the Father and of the Son!

HENRY. (to JOHNNY) This is nothing but a dream, it's
only a dream ... a little naive maybe, but what do I
care.

JOHNNY. That's right! What do you care whether or not
it's a dream ... as long as it gives you pleasure.

51

HENRY. Pleasure.

(Meanwhile, the FATHER, MOTHER, MOLLY and
the DIGNITARIES gather around him)

MOTHER. Oh, look how he's blushing.

FATHER. Ha, ha, ha! He's ashamed ... Now, now, Henry,
look at me, look at me ...

HENRY. What for?

FATHER. Because tomorrow's the wedding ...

HENRY. But I don't understand ...

FATHER. (aside) Tssst ... Surely you're not going to fool
around with some cheap tupenny ha'penny whore, not
when you have the chance to marry a respectable
young lady ... In our family it has always been the
custom to have a respectable marriage. Your mother
and I were married in a proper manner, and it is
only fitting that you do the same ... You'll see everything will turn out all right ... (In a loud voice) Thank
you, my son, for showing me your affection ... Soon
we shall be celebrating your marriage and with it my
joy and that of your mother, my spouse, and as for
that which is already past, squandered and forgotten,
we simply won't talk about that any more, as far
as we're concerned it never happened, it no longer
is, it isn't ...

MOTHER. (in a very loud voice) Alleluia!

(Music, wedding march. FATHER and MOTHER,
HENRY and MOLLY, JOHNNY and the DIGNITARIES
march around the stage in a solemn and cordial
procession)

HENRY. (in a very loud voice)
Is it possible to imagine anything more improbable
Than this farcical march of phantoms in a fog of
illusion?

52

And yet does it fill my breast with glee and cause
   my poor heart to sing
When me to my former lover this festive march
   does bring.
(To everyone) Forgive me, I am a rhymester.

MOTHER.
    It's such times as these that gladden a mother's
      heart,
    Which for so many years has stood in disregard!

FATHER.
    The music is playing, the couples in procession
    As once was the custom in times gone by!
    Follow me, gentlemen! As God is our Protector!
    Don't stop, gentlemen! Come on!
    March forward! Forward! Come on, let's go!
    Faster, faster! Keep in step!
    Step lively, gentlemen! March in style!
    Don't fall behind! March forward!
    Forward! Forward! Come on, let's go!
    (He notices the DRUNKARD)
    Stop, stop, stop! He's come here to gawp at us!
    Seize this man, arrest him and throw him into
    Some dark and dreary, foul and fetid, godforsaken
      dungeon!
    (To the DRUNKARD) I'm going to let you have it,
      see!

DRUNKARD.
    I'm going to let you have it, see!

FATHER.
    You?
    Me?

DRUNKARD.
    I'll touch you yet ...
    (To MOLLY) Isn't that right, Miss Molly?

FATHER. You pig!

DRUNKARD. You pig!

FATHER. You pig!

ACT TWO

(A large room, in semi-darkness)

HENRY. (leaning up against a column)
      O to divine
      The sense of this dream ...

      (Two by two the DIGNITARIES pass by in the penum-
      bra and mount the stairs to an elevated platform which
      fades away in the darkness)

1st DIGNITARY.
      A maidservant who served to render service!

2nd DIGNITARY.
      And the king of the tavern is a tangible tavern-
          keeper!

      (They pass by)

3rd DIGNITARY.
      The wedding will take place shortly.

4th DIGNITARY.
      The wedding? That's a joke!

      (They pass by)

5th DIGNITARY. How much longer must we go on making
      asses of ourselves, poking our noses into this servant
      girl's business?

6th DIGNITARY. And that drunkard has broken loose from
      his shackles and is roaming about the neighbourhood.

(They pass by. The FATHER approaches)

HENRY. Father!

FATHER. Yes, it's me, Henry ... They're getting ready
for the marriage. In a minute we're going to give you
a wedding that'll make everybody green with envy ...
(Pointing into the darkness) They're making preparations over there now. Just keep a firm grip on yourself!

HENRY. What kind of a marriage? Who will perform the
ceremony, where and how?

FATHER. Who? The Bishop. I've sent for the Bishop to
make sure everything goes the way it should. Don't
worry. I've taken care of everything, but don't lose
your head, Henry, don't lose your head ... and for
God's sake don't do anything stupid - otherwise the
marriage will be a flop ... Remember, it's not
just your father who's involved here - there's your
sweetheart to consider too ...

HENRY. (into space) Sometimes I think this is all very
wise, and other times ...

FATHER. Tssst ... But whatever you do, Henry, don't
betray me, because there are enough traitors around
here already ... Don't try to make a laughingstock
out of me, Henry, I beg of you ... because the place
is crawling with traitors ... traitors ... traitors
... Traitors! (He withdraws, then climbs up to the
platform)

HENRY. I don't know what my feelings are!

(Light. FATHER appears on the platform surrounded
by a COUNCIL AND COURT. The faces of the DIG-
NITARIES are expressive to the point of caricature,
wise, slightly contemptuous; the costumes are magnificent but border on the burlesque)

What majesty! (He goes before the throne)

58

Here I am!

FATHER. Henry!

COUNCIL AND COURT. Oh, Henry!

HENRY. Oh, Henry!

FATHER.
Henry, my son, we are about to embark
Upon your nuptial ceremony. Soon
Will the bridal party usher in the maid
With whom you'll be united world without end
Amen, amen.

MOTHER. (fervently)
Amen.

CHANCELLOR. (wisely and venerably)
Amen.
That was a grave and lofty speech.

DIGNITARY/TRAITOR. (aside)
Amen.
That was an asinine and ridiculous speech.

FATHER. (as though frightened)
I say

It will take place immediately. In a moment. Because it must take place, I decreed it, I proclaimed it
... And if anybody tries to stand in the way! ... Out,
out, you filthy maggots, out, out, you good-for-
nothing bums!

Oh, oh, gentlemen of my council! A short while ago
A pack of these slimy, rotten, low-down,
Stinking, slobbering, soused-up sows
Attacked me and tried to touch
My person!

COUNCIL AND COURT.
Oh, my God!

FATHER.
Even though I am the King!

COUNCIL AND COURT.
Oh, my God!

FATHER.
Even though I am untouchable!

COUNCIL AND COURT.
For heaven's sake!

FATHER. (heavily, sclerotically) Oh, woe, woe! What a
terrible sacrilege, what an intolerable, unthinkable,
unpardonable blasphemy! And that's not all. I hear
that sow of a souse has broken loose from his shackles
while his guards were out getting pickled ... Chancellor of my Council, command that the gates be
closed and have the guards put on alert - there's no
telling what these drunks will do. I have an itch.
Command that the gates be closed!

DIGNITARY/TRAITOR. (unexpectedly, brazenly)
Ha, ha, ha! That's impossible!
Ha, ha, ha!

TRAITORS. Ha, ha, ha!

FATHER. What do you mean?

DIGNITARY/TRAITOR. Forgive me, Your Majesty, forgive
me, Your Majesty, but His Majesty can't just close
his gates to any old drunk who happens to come along,
since that would mean His Majesty is afraid of any
old drunk and that would be unthinkable because that
would constitute an affront to His Majesty, and His
Majesty cannot commit an affront to the majesty of
His Majesty ...

TRAITORS. Well said!

FATHER.
What, what, what?

I only mentioned it because that drunken swine has
been getting more aggressive lately ... but if it's
impossible, then it's impossible. Don't stretch your
luck, you pigs! I know what you've got up your sleeves!

> I have no need of such measures
> Because this ceremony will be so ceremonious
> So dignified, so respectable and so majestic
> In all its majestical majesty, that
> No scum on earth would have the nerve to ...
> (Intoxicated) Sound the trumpets
> Because the son for the greater glory of his father
> Is about to enter the marital state
> By virtue of my royal decree, yes
> By my most sovereign decree
> Now on with it, on with it!
> Come on, let's go!

COUNCIL AND COURT.   (standing up with fury)
> On with it! On with it!
> Come on, let's go!

FATHER. Stop, stop, everything must be arranged before-
hand, so everything goes the way it should ... I have
an itch. Chancellor of my Council, scratch me. Where
is the ceremonial cloak? Put the ceremonial cloak
and grand-ducal hat on my son and gird him with the
sacred sword!

2nd DIGNITARY. Amen.

3rd DIGNITARY. That was wise.

DIGNITARY/TRAITOR. (aside) That was silly as a goose!

2nd DIGNITARY. Our noble young man will look powerful
and magnificent in these vestments.

DIGNITARY/TRAITOR. Comical and idiotic, but that's his
affair.

(Pause)

HENRY. Do I really have to put all that on? (JOHNNY hands him the vestments) Oh, is that you, Johnny?

JOHNNY. It's me.

HENRY. Who are you, that is to say, what are you?

JOHNNY. (clumsily, as though embarrassed) I've been assigned to your service, Your ... Your Highness ...

HENRY. I can't talk to you. I feel awkward ... Hand me my hat. I look funny, eh?

JOHNNY. Yes and no.

HENRY. Now gird me with the sacred sword. This is a joke, but it doesn't matter. The main thing is I'm going to marry her. (Suddenly this dialogue becomes public, as though both had forgotten about the presence of the KING and COURT)

JOHNNY.
Of course it doesn't matter
The main thing is you're going to marry her.

HENRY.
I have to adapt myself to the circumstances, but
    don't think for a moment
That I take any of this nonsense seriously.
I do it more out of curiosity, I'm anxious to see
What the outcome will be, besides what harm can
    it do me
To amuse myself ...

JOHNNY.
That's the spirit
It's better to amuse yourself
Than to be bored ...

HENRY. That's it exactly!

(HENRY turns to the KING in his ceremonial attire; laughter of the TRAITORS; derisory names are flung

62

        down at him)

1st TRAITOR. Clown!

2nd TRAITOR. Buffoon!

3rd TRAITOR. Imbecile!

FATHER. (in a vulgar manner)
          Aaaah, shuut up!
          Keep your bloody traps shut!
          I didn't give anyone permission to speak!
          I give the floor to my son
          Let him speak. (Panic-stricken) Henreee, say
            something!

HENRY. What'll I say?

FATHER. (in absolute terror) Henree, say something, but
         for the love of God, say something clever ... say
         something clever! Shuut up, pigs! Now you're going to
         see how my son can talk ... he'll put you in your
         places, he'll teach you a thing or two. Come on,
         Henreee, say something, but something clever, say
         something clever, because if you don't then ... then
         ...

HENRY. Then what?

FATHER. That's just what they're waiting for!

        (General expectation)

DIGNITARY/TRAITOR. He will speak foolishly, because
        he looks foolish.

2nd DIGNITARY. He will speak cleverly, because he looks
        clever.

        (General expectation)

HENRY.
        Honestly

I don't know what to say, but I shall soon find out
What I will have said.

1st GROUP. What a brilliant idea!

2nd GROUP. What an idiotic idea!

HENRY. (musingly)
I am foolish
And yet I am to speak cleverly ...

ALL. Here comes a confession ...

HENRY. (with sincerity)
Again do my words
Acquire extraordinary power, while I stand here
by myself
And speak to you alone. But what should I say?

(To himself) If I say something wise, it will sound
foolish, because I am foolish. And if I say something
foolish ...

FATHER. No, no, Henreee!

HENRY. (to himself) If I'm unable to uphold the grandeur of
this majesty, this majesty will sink to the level of
my buffoonery. I can't think of anything clever to
say - just the same old empty thoughts and words ...
Wait a minute! Now I know what I will say.

(To everyone) My words are vapid
But they reverberate off you
And become magnified by your majesty -
Not by the majesty of the one who speaks
But by the majesty of the one who listens.

1st GROUP.
Well spoken!
Wisely spoken!

HENRY.
I am talking nonsense
But you are listening wisely to me, and hence

64

I am becoming wise.

COUNCIL AND COURT. Wisdom! Wisdom!

MOTHER. What a mind he has, eh?

HENRY.
    I have no dignity
    I lost my dignity a long time ago. But my father
    Has elevated me to a new dignity now. And so I'm
      becoming
    Wiser and more dignified than I am. And I accept it,
    Yes, I accept it. I do hereby proclaim
    That I wish to be married in a manner sublime.
    So let's get on with it! Where is she?
    Show her in and forward, forward!

COUNCIL AND COURT. (standing up, with fury)
    Wisdom! Dignity! Marriage! On with it!
    Forward, forward, forward!

FATHER. (thunderously) With wisdom profound and dignity
    sublime has my son expounded. Open the gates and
    bring in the bride and His Holiness the Bishop, and let
    the trumpets trumpet with all their might into the very
    heart of nature; let the trumpets trumpet, I say, so as
    to terrify and terrorize any pig who's piggish enough
    to pig up the works, because there's no dearth of these
    dirty pigs and ... aaah, the pigggs, the pigggs, the
    pigggggggs ...

    (Trumpets. MOLLY, dressed in a sumptuous gown,
    comes in together with the BRIDAL PARTY; through
    another door enters BISHOP PANDULF followed by his
    retinue)

FATHER. Henreee!

COUNCIL AND COURT. Oh, Henry!

HENRY. Oh, Henry!

FATHER. (in a choked voice, as though frightened) We are
    about to begin ... In our family it has always been

the custom to have a respectable marriage. Don't cry, mother. (To MOLLY and HENRY) All right, both of you stand over here ... bow your heads ... (Aloud) We are about to embark upon the most holy act of matrimony, in the name of the Father and of the Son ... (Aside) Kneel down and let the trumpets trumpet ... Let the bridesmaids take the train in their hands ... Chancellor, hand me my sceptre ... put on my crown ... (Aloud) In the name of the Father and of the Son. (Aside) And now His Holiness the Bishop will bind their hands with the holy sash as proof of this

> Crushing, shattering,
> Omnipotent act performed
> In the presence of our majesty! Sound the trumpets!
> Hand us the holy sash! Down on your knees!
> Oh, Lord! Help! My good people!
> So be it! And so it shall be! Such is my decree!
> Such is my will!

DIGNITARY/TRAITOR. (loudly, insolently) Treason!

(The DRUNKARD staggers in)

FATHER. (stupidly) Heyyy ... what's going on here?

(A long silence)

DRUNKARD. I beg your pardon ... It's nothing ... I was just ...

FATHER. (terrified) Ask this man who gave him permission to come in here and have him removed at once.

DRUNKARD. A bottle of vodka, a fifth, some gin, four bottles of beer and a herring sandwich!

A VOICE. He's drunk ...

2nd VOICE. To the gills ...

(General laughter, sighs of relief)

HENRY.
>I do not know this man, and yet
>I have the feeling I do know him ...
>(With solemn meekness)
>But in any case
>I cannot help knowing
>Everything which is happening here ...

FATHER.
>He's drunk ...
>Throw him out, take him away, show him the door
>...

CHANCELLOR. (approaches the DRUNKARD) What are you
doing here, my good man? Do you not realize that
you are standing in the presence of His Royal Majesty?

DRUNKARD. Ai-yai-yai ... His Majesty the King! Good
heavens!

FATHER.
>All right, all right, that'll do,
>You are in luck, my good fellow, you have seen
> the King
>Now go on home and sleep it off.
>Oh, how distressing is this disease of drink
>That brings our people closer to the brink!

COURT. Oh, indeed! Indeed!

CHANCELLOR. Here, buy yourself a drink, now buzz off!
... Why don't you go away?

(The following utterances should be pronounced with
an air of perfunctoriness, apathy)

DIGNITARY/TRAITOR. Why don't you go away?

DRUNKARD. Because I can't.

2nd DIGNITARY. You can't?

DRUNKARD. I can't.

3rd DIGNITARY. And why can't you?

DRUNKARD. Because I feel funny.

CHANCELLOR. (to the FATHER)
The poor fellow's embarrassed, he can't move
He doesn't know how to behave, ha, ha, ha!

FATHER.
Ha, ha, ha!

CHANCELLOR.
Ha, ha, ha!
(Indicating the door with his finger)
Beat it, I tell you!

DRUNKARD. (with awe)
A finger!

CHANCELLOR.
Beat it!

DRUNKARD.
A finger!

CHANCELLOR.
Out!

DRUNKARD.
What a finger!

COURT.
Ha, ha, ha, a finger, a finger!

DRUNKARD. (examining his finger) It's not like mine ...
Mine is vulgar, grubby-looking ... a domestic finger,
a peasant's finger ... just right for nose-picking.

(Laughter)

A coarse finger, the finger of a village clod ... why
it's an insult even to display such a finger before such
august personages ...

CHANCELLOR. Get out of here!

DRUNKARD. Okay, okay, I'm going, but I can't because everyone's staring at my finger.

DIGNITARY/TRAITOR. Why don't you stick it in your pocket?

VOICES.
    Stick it in your ear!
    Or stick it in your eye!

DRUNKARD. I'd like to put it away, but I can't because everyone's looking at it! If I so much as point at something with this finger (inadvertently points at HENRY) then right away everybody looks to see what it is I'm pointing at.

HENRY. (softly)
    Pig ...

DRUNKARD. (softly)
    Pig ...

    (Aloud) They're gawping at my finger as if it were somehow extraordinary! And the more they look, the more extraordinary it becomes, and the more extraordinary it becomes, the more they look and the more they look, the more extraordinary it becomes, and the more extraordinary it becomes, the more they look, and the more they look, the more Extraordinary it becomes ...

    This is an extraordinary finger!
    This is a powerful Finger!
    Oh, how they've pumped up my finger!

    And if I now decided to ... to toushhh someone with this finger ...

FATHER. Shut up!

DRUNKARD. - even though that person is untoushhable ...

69

FATHER. Shut up!

DRUNKARD. (brutally) And once I toushh, I get cocky!

TRAITORS. Go ahead! On with it! On with it!

FATHER. (shouting) Pig!

DRUNKARD. (shouting) Pig!

FATHER. (in a very calm voice)
          Friends, gentlemen of my Council and personages
          Of my person ...
          (He bursts out) Hold on to me, I'm exploding!
          (Frightened by his own outburst) I'm bursting ...
            I'm exploding ...
          I'm bursting out in such horrifying,
          Terrifying anger, that ... oh ... oh ... oh ...
          (Feebly) I feel weak ...

MOTHER. Frankie! He feels weak!

COURT. The King feels weak! The King is sick!

FATHER. (feebly, imploringly)
          Henreee ...

COUNCIL AND COURT. (powerfully)
          Oh, Henry!

HENRY. Oh, Henry!

          Henry, in the name of the Father, in the name of
            the Son
          In the name of the Father and of the Son!

(HENRY approaches the DRUNKARD whose finger has
been dominating the scene)

          You pig!

DRUNKARD. You pig!

70

HENRY. (calmly)
　　You pig!
　　Put that finger away!

DRUNKARD. (drunk) I don't know what you're talking about!

HENRY. Put it away, or else I'll put it away for you!

DRUNKARD. A bottle of booze!

HENRY. Put it away or I'll pounce on it and put it away
　　myself ... I'll pounce on it ... (A moment later)
　　Look how idiotically it sticks out ... right in the
　　middle of everything ... No, I can't pounce on it ...
　　because the whole thing is preposterous ... it's too
　　silly for words ...

TRAITORS. (sharply)
　　Silly!
　　Silly as a goose!

HENRY. Stop, stop! I'm not silly, - it's that finger which is
　　silly! He stuck it out on purpose so as to make a mockery
　　of everything - to make me out to be a lunatic!

DRUNKARD. (pointing at HENRY) Lunatic!

TRAITORS. Lunatic!

HENRY. Be careful, I'm warning you ... Don't exasperate
　　me, or I shall wake up ... and you will all disappear
　　... (To MOLLY) You will disappear too ...

(Silence. The stage becomes motionless)

　　But perhaps
　　This is not a dream, perhaps I really have gone
　　crazy

Perhaps I'm not here at all, but in reality I'm lying
in some hospital, and while feverishly thrashing
about, I only imagine that I am here ... Who knows
what might have happened to me?

71

Perhaps my brain has been damaged by a bullet?
Or by an explosion?
Perhaps I've been taken captive and tortured, or
    perhaps
I fell on something, or something fell on me
Perhaps I became bored ... and was no longer
    able ...

Or perhaps they ordered me - despatched me - forced
me to do something which I couldn't bear. No, there
is not a single thing which might not have happened to
me - everything and even more than everything is
possible. But suppose I am not in a hospital and nothing
abnormal has happened to me. All right ... and yet ...
Oh, how many insanities have I taken part in?

Ohhh ...
Even though I was the most healthy ... the most
    rational
The most balanced person
Others forced me to commit
Atrocious acts, murderous acts,
Insane, moronic, and yes, licentious acts ...

This raises a simple question: If in the course of
several years a person fulfills the function of a madman,
is he not then really a madman? And what does it
matter that I am healthy if my actions are sick - eh
Johnny? But those who forced me to commit these
insanities were also healthy

And sensible
And balanced ... Friends, companions, brothers -
    so much
Health
And such sick behaviour? So much sanity
And yet so much madness? So much humanity

And yet so much inhumanity? And what does it matter
if taken separately each of us is lucid, sensible,
balanced, when altogether we are nothing but a gigantic
madman who furiously

Writhes about, screams, bellows and blindly
Rushes forward, overstepping his own bounds
Ripping himself out of himself ... Our madness
Is outside ourselves, out there ... There, there,
    out there.
Where I myself end, there begins
My wantonness ... And even though I live in peace
Within myself, still do I wander outside myself
And in dark, wild spaces and nocturnal places
Surrender myself to some unbounded chaos!

CHANCELLOR. This is a funeral march!

FATHER. This is a funeral march!

HENRY.
    That's it, a funeral march!
    Once again they have spoken. And I have spoken,
    And this finger is jutting out in the middle like the
        finger of a lunatic
    And here I am talking to myself and gesticulating
        in absolute solitude like a lunatic ...

DRUNKARD. Lunatic!

TRAITORS. Lunatic!

(They advance toward HENRY)

HENRY. Stay where you are! I am here at the King's behest.

DRUNKARD. The King is a lunatic!

HENRY.
    Stop!

    Suppose my father has gone mad, but in his madness
    he is still a defender of virtue and dignity - in which
    case he can't be mad!
    Yes, that's the truth, that's the most truthful truth -
    and hence that solemnity, wisdom, and gravity which
    have descended upon me. Look how wisely I am
    standing! My wisdom and my dignity are invincible!

And he just stands there with his finger like an imbecile!
Go ahead - I dare you to touch me!

FATHER.
     Henry!

COUNCIL AND COURT.
     Oh, Henry!

HENRY.
     Oh, Henry! ...
     Throw that drunkard out of here!

(The DIGNITARIES advance toward the DRUNKARD)

DRUNKARD. (slowly, putting his finger away) Hey, not so
     rough, eh? ... I'm an intelligent person too ... (He
     suddenly becomes exceedingly clever. To HENRY)

     I'm not half
     As dumb as you think ...

     (A moment later) What d'you say you and I have a
     little talk on the side, eh? You know - one wise man
     to another ...

HENRY. (startled) What about?

DRUNKARD. We'll see. We'll have a wise little chat ...
     (To everyone) Because I'm a wise man, too ...

HENRY. (hesitantly)
     No. Although ...
     If he wants to talk wisely ...

DIGNITARY/TRAITOR. (provokingly)
     If he wants to talk wisely ...

COURT. (somnolently)
     If
     if
     wisely ...

74

HENRY. Very well!

(Afternoon tea. LACKEYS bring in coffee and pastries.
The DIGNITARIES break up into groups. The LADIES
fan themselves with enormous fans)

COURT.

How pleasant it is at His Majesty's tea
To carry on a flirt in a form so discreet
Oh, the toupees and decolletes do the senses arouse
While His Majesty himself does the honours of the
        house!

May I offer you some pastires? That's very kind of
you. Oh, what a splendid crowd! I'm terribly sorry.
I bow down before you. Oh, what a magnificent gown!

VOICE OF THE FATHER. (upstage) All right, give me a
    little tea too!

A LADY. (passing by, to a DIGNITARY) Who is that strange
    looking character talking with the Crown Prince?

A DIGNITARY. He's a foreign envoy or else an ambassador.

HENRY. All right, give me a little tea too. (To the DRUNK-
    ARD) May I offer you some pastries?

DRUNKARD. That's very kind of you. I hope nobody is
    listening.

HENRY. As you can see, they're going out of their way
    to make this little chat possible ... in absolute
    secrecy ...

(They both walk over to one side of the stage)

DRUNKARD. Well, I'll come straight to the point ... I'm
    not quite as drunk as I appear to be ... and all these
    antics of mine are part of a plot to undermine the
    authority of the King. Many of the dignitaries are
    conspiring against him, and it was they who dragged
    me out of prison by the scruff of the neck. But Your

Highness spoke just now with such wisdom that ...

HENRY.
He's trying to flatter me ...

DRUNKARD. ... that all my efforts were for nothing.
There was only one thing in all this wisdom which
struck me as being not quite so wise ... Do you
believe in God, Your Highness?

HENRY. (into space)
Since he has asked, I have to say no.

DRUNKARD. Well, then how can you let yourself be
married by the King? If God does not exist, how can
your father be a king? After all, doesn't his power
come from God? And this Bishop is not a bishop on
his own power either.

HENRY. I already told you ... I already answered that ...
Even if my father were an ordinary madman who only
imagined he was King, he is still a defender of virtue
and dignity ... And even though I do not believe in
God, I do believe in Moral Law and Human Dignity on
earth.

How solemn I sound!

DRUNKARD. And who established that law if there isn't
any God?

HENRY. Who? People.

DRUNKARD. Then why do you wish to make this such a
solemn occasion if it is merely a product of man's
imagination like everything else?

HENRY. (flustered)
As a matter of fact
To a certain extent he's right. I don't believe
In any of this ... I behave
As though I believed in it, and yet I don't believe
in it

76

I respect it, and yet I don't respect it ... I gen-
uflect
But I don't genuflect ... I humble myself
And yet I don't humble myself
And I know that all of this is just a farce. And so
The greater my wisdom, the greater
My stupidity ... Shhh! Shhh! Quiet!
He mustn't find out about this!

DRUNKARD. Why does Your Highness place him above
yourself if it was you who put him on the throne in
the first place?

HENRY. (to himself) That's true. And if he is not my King,
I am not his Prince ...

DRUNKARD. And the same is true of your fiancee ... If it
was you who made him King, and if it was the King
who elevated her to the dignity of a virgin, that would
mean it was you, Your Highness, who made a virgin
out of her ... And what kind of a virgin is that, I ask
you?

HENRY. It was I who made a virgin out of her. This
drunkard has a pretty clear head on his shoulders
... And yet

If it were really that simple, why
Do I feel as though I were celebrating
Some sort of elevated mass?

DRUNKARD. A mass?

HENRY. A mass.

DRUNKARD. A mass?

HENRY. A mass.

(Gravely) Get away from me: I am a priest ...

DRUNKARD. (slowly) I am a priest too ...

COURT.
>   Oh, the toupees and decolletes do the senses arouse
>   While His Majesty himself does the honours of the
>   house!

HENRY. (sadly) He's mimicking me, he's mimicking me
>   so as to make a fool out of me. A moment ago he
>   was talking sense, but now he's talking nonsense ...

DRUNKARD. Nonsense?

HENRY. (thoughtful) Nonsense. I thought he was more
>   clever ...

DRUNKARD. Clever?

HENRY. Clever.

DRUNKARD. Clever?

HENRY. Clever!

DRUNKARD. (exploding)
>   Now I shall tell you something and cleverly, too
>   About that religion whose priests we both are.
>   Between ourselves
>   And through ourselves is our God born
>   And not to heaven, but to earth does our church
>   belong
>   We create God and we alone, whence does arise
>   That dark and terrestrial, ignorant and bestial
>   Intimate and inferior, humanly human mass
>   Whose priest I am!

(Both PRIESTS begin making wild and pathetic
gestures)

HENRY.
>   Whose priest I am?
>   But ... I don't understand.

DRUNKARD.
>   You don't understand

78

And yet somehow you do understand. You understand
Because I understand.

HENRY.

You understand
Because I understand. You? Me? Which of us
No, no, I don't exactly see ...

DRUNKARD.

Do you see
This finger? (He shows him his finger)

HENRY.

Do you see
This finger? (He shows him his finger)

DRUNKARD.

Yes, I see it
I see that finger!

HENRY.

And I see it too!
Oh, what wisdom, what profundity! It's as though
I were looking at myself in a thousand mirrors!
Your finger, my finger!

DRUNKARD.

My finger, your finger, your finger, my finger!
  Between ourselves.
It's between ourselves. Would you like me
To anoint you priest
With this finger?

HENRY.

Would you like me
To anoint you priest
With this finger?

DRUNKARD.

Oh, yes, gladly.

HENRY.

Oh, yes, gladly.

(The DRUNKARD makes as if to touch him)

There's that finger again! You pig!

DRUNKARD. You pig!

HENRY. You pig!

All he ever wants to do is touch me!
(Checking himself) May I offer you some pastry?

COURT.

How pleasant it is at His Majesty's tea
To carry on a flirt in a form so discreet
Oh, the toupees and decolletes do the senses arouse
While His Majesty himself does the honours of the
house!

HENRY. (to himself) Oh, I let myself be taken in by
words, and all this time he just wanted to touch me.
I'd touch this moron who's been trying to make a moron
out of me ... I'd touch him and throw him out, but
there are too many lights here, too many women and
too many dignitaries. (He makes for the DRUNKARD,
but the DIGNITARIES intervene)

DIGNITARY/TRAITOR. (to the DRUNKARD) My dear
Ambassador!

A LADY. (passing by) Who is that mysterious gentleman
who has been chatting with the Crown Prince for such
a long time?

A DIGNITARY. (emphatically) He's a foreign envoy or
else an ambassador!

A LADY. An ambassador!

DIGNITARY/TRAITOR. My dear Ambassador!

2nd TRAITOR. Dear Mr. Ambassador!

3rd TRAITOR. My dearest Ambassador!

DRUNKARD. (eloquently)
    Ah, greetings, gentlemen, greetings!

A LADY.
    My dearest Ambassador Plenipotentiary!

DRUNKARD.
    I bow down before you, madam.

    (Ceremonious bows)

HENRY. Hmmm ... A few minutes ago he was just a
    drunkard, and now he's an ambassador. I'd touch
    him, but I have no desire to make a fool of myself.
    One has to keep up appearances.

DRUNKARD. Forgive me, ladies and gentlemen, but I
    would like to have just a few more words with the
    Crown Prince. Then I shall be completely at your
    service.

TRAITORS. We shall not disturb you, Your Excellency.
    (Deep bows; they withdraw)

DRUNKARD. (to HENRY) This is indeed a magnificent
    reception!

HENRY. Indeed it is.

COURT.
    Oh, the toupees and decolletes do the senses arouse
    While His Majesty himself does the honours of the
        house!

    (The AMBASSADOR and the PRINCE stroll back and
    forth with this elegant reception in the background)

DRUNKARD. (in the style of a diplomat) In regard to what
    we were just saying, His Highness will be pleased to
    observe ... Please believe me when I say that albeit
    I am a foreign ambassador, still do I harbour the most
    fervent feelings of devotion and respect for the person
    of His Royal Majesty. On the other hand, I should

say it is precisely on account of this feeling of love and respect that I fear ... or rather, I suspect ... and to a certain extent even know ... that many of your eminent dignitaries have of late estranged themselves, so to speak, from the throne ...

HENRY. (diplomatically) Is that so?

DRUNKARD. As a sincere friend and devoted servant of the royal family I consider it well-nigh my duty to apprise Your Highness of this state of affairs in a confidential manner.

HENRY. I am extremely indebted to you, Mr. Ambassador.

DRUNKARD. There is no question, Your Highness, but that your father is a great monarch, or so it would seem to me at least ... but it is not at all inconceivable, I am afraid, that his concept of power is not altogether consistent with the spirit of modern times.

DIGNITARY/TRAITOR. You could not have couched it any better, Mr. Ambassador.

DRUNKARD. That he is a grand and imposing figure cannot be disputed, but the anachronism of his concepts is all too evident - an anachronism, I might add, which is peculiar to persons more advanced in years. (In a confidential manner) But really, Your Highness - to believe in some code of morality and decency that has been laid down once and for all? Between you and me, modern man must be exceedingly more flexible; modern man knows that there is nothing permanent or absolute, but that everything is forever creating itself anew ... creating itself between individuals ... creating itself ...

HENRY. One cannot deny that you are a flexible person and that you are constantly creating yourself anew ...

DRUNKARD. Looking at it objectively ... But let's have something to drink, eh? To His Majesty's health!

DIGNITARY/TRAITOR. To His Majesty's health!

HENRY. To His Majesty's health!

DRUNKARD. Let's see, what were we talking about? ...
    Ah, yes ... It is for that very reason that not a few
    of the dignitaries have, so to say, estranged them-
    selves ... ha, ha, ha, but His Majesty's greatest
    enemy is yourself, Your Highness ...

HENRY. Me?

DRUNKARD. Ha, ha, ha! Because the admiration which
    your noble qualities arouse ...

HENRY. He's trying to flatter me ...

DRUNKARD. (in a confidential manner) Many people here
    believe you are the one who ought to be in power ...
    But let's have something to drink, eh Prince? To
    His Majesty's health!

DIGNITARY/TRAITOR. To His Majesty's health! Many
    people here have no other desire - after a very long
    life for His Majesty - save that of seeing you in power
    ...

DRUNKARD. And then His Highness could grant himself
    a marriage ... or even do without a marriage alto-
    gether, ha, ha, ha - instead of submitting to these
    old-fashioned ceremonies!

DIGNITARY/TRAITOR. Let's have another glass! Goodness
    but that wine is strong ... it makes one teeter ...
    like a king on his throne ...

DRUNKARD. Ha, ha, ha! As a matter of fact, it seems it
    would suffice to touch glasses!

DIGNITARY/TRAITOR. To touch glasses in the presence
    of the entire Court!

DRUNKARD. Then, if someone touched the King ...

DIGNITARY/TRAITOR. Quite unexpectedly!

DRUNKARD. Touched ...

DIGNITARY/TRAITOR. Just like that, in front of everybody! For all to see!

DRUNKARD. Ha, ha, ha! But nobody's going to touch the
King because everyone is afraid of the Prince's
anger and wisdom. It's only natural for a son to
defend his father ...

DIGNITARY/TRAITOR. Another glass! But what if the
Prince himself ... if the Prince himself went up to
him and ... I didn't really mean that, though you
must admit it's a tempting idea ... I confess that
whenever I see such an untouchable person ... damn
it, I don't know why, I always get the urge ... to go
up and ... er ... well ... touch him, see? With
my finger. Hm, hm ...

DRUNKARD. Ha, ha, ha, ha, ha! And there's his fiancee
standing behind him and, damn it, she's untouchable
too ... Untouchable! Oh, if I could just touch him
with one finger at least, with just one little finger,
oh, oh, oh, and ha, ha, ha!

HENRY.
　　　Finger!
　　　(calmly) There's that idiotic finger again!
　　　You pig!

DRUNKARD. (gloomily)
　　　You pig!

HENRY.
　　　You pig!
　　　May I offer you some pastry?

COURT.
　　　How pleasant it is at His Majesty's tea
　　　To carry on a flirt in a form so discreet ...

HENRY.
> And you would like me
> To touch the King ... with my finger ... Because
> if I touch the King
> Then you'll touch him too, right? ... You'd have
> me
> Commit treason ... is that it?

BOTH.
> Oh, oh!
> That was just the wine in us speaking ... A drop
> of that stuff
> And a man's liable to say anything!

HENRY. You bloody drunken swine, you're trying to get
me drunk ... Well, in a second I'll prove to you and
to myself how sober I am ... that's right, sober.
This intrigue is absurd. But this absurdity is likewise
deceiving. Because this intrigue is so irrational,
so obviously contrived that even if I rejected your
rather naive propositions, in the end I would come
out looking just as ridiculous as if I'd agreed to them.
That's what you had in mind all along, isn't it? And
so I hereby declare both to you and to myself that I
regard none of this seriously - neither you, nor this
conversation, nor the title of this man who only a
short while ago was nothing but an ordinary drunkard.
I don't give a damn about the lot of you! And if I stand
here talking to you instead of pouncing on you and
touching you - it's only because I wish to keep up
appearances and, if possible, avoid a scandal ... So
there! Am I sober or not?

DRUNKARD.
> A glass of Burgundy or a glass of Tokay!

DIGNITARY/TRAITOR.
> A glass of Tokay or a glass of port!

HENRY. Of course I'm sober! I could wake up at any
moment and annihilate you all - but I don't wish to
spoil this magnificent and intoxicating reception ...
and besides, then my fiancee would disappear too,

evaporate ... Understand?

DRUNKARD.
    Burgundy, Burgundy!

DIGNITARY/TRAITOR.
    Tokay, Tokay!

HENRY. I am the most sober person in the world! I am
behaving in the same manner as you are, but with
full awareness, soberly, ha, ha, ha ... I am behaving in the same manner as you are, because to tell
the truth, all of this gives me pleasure ...

    Words tickle me, thoughts caress me, the passions
      get stronger
    Everything is spinning ... singing ... ringing
    Oh, this sea of lights, this ocean of words
    And I'm drowning in it, drowning, drowning ...
      like a drunkard
    (See how sober I am!?)
    I'm unsteady on my feet and I'm seeing three of
      everything
    I'm hearing things and my vision's getting blurry
    It's almost as though I understood, but I don't
      understand ...
    Noise. Noise. And in this noise
    One thought alone persists: keep up appearances

    Don't let anyone catch on you're drunk, ha, ha (See
how lucid I am!?) and don't let anyone know you're
a drunkard.
    And so, if anyone addresses me in a polite tone, I'll
answer him with extreme politeness, ah, ah, yes,
yes!
    And if anyone begins speaking to me in a serious
tone, ho, ho, yes indeed, yes indeed!
    And if anyone starts behaving toward me like a
drunkard, I'll behave toward him like a drunkard too,
hee, hee, hic, hic! (You can see for yourselves how
lucid I am ...)

DRUNKARD. (drunk)
    Son-of-a ... oh, f-f-f-fiddlesticks!

86

Shit!

HENRY.
        Wait a minute, wait a minute
        I'll show you even more clearly how sober I am.
          Let's assume
        You are soused too - and that everyone here
        Is a little ... hmm ... One person gets drunk by
          means of another
        While each would pretend he's as sober as I. Ha,
          ha, ha!
        But if that were the case, then this is all a farce!

One drunkard, in order to pretend he's sober, adapts
himself to the drunkenness of another who, in order to
pretend he's sober, adapts himself to the drunkenness
of still another drunkard who ...

        And consequently all of this is just a lie! Nobody
          says
        What he wants to say, only what's considered
          proper. Words
        Join together behind our backs like traitors
        And it is not we who say words, but words which
          say us
        And betray our thoughts, which in turn betray
        Our treasonous feelings ... Oh, treason!
        (Drunk) Incessant treason!

DRUNKARD. (picking up the thread) That's right, treason!

DIGNITARY/TRAITOR.
        Treason! Down with the King!
        Down with the King!

TRAITORS. (gathering around them, in an undertone)
        Down with the King!

HENRY. Traitors! That's not what I wanted to say!

DIGNITARY/TRAITOR. (in the voice of a conspirator)
        Gentlemen, the Prince is with us! Down with the
          King!

Long live the new King!

DRUNKARD. Down with the King!

(HENRY and the CONSPIRATORS advance toward the
KING. The GUESTS make way, revealing the KING,
who is taking his tea in the company of the QUEEN
and MOLLY. JOHNNY is standing nearby)

HENRY. That's not what I wanted to say!

COURT.
How pleasant it is at His Majesty's tea
To carry on a flirt in a form so discreet
Oh, the toupees and decolletes do the senses arouse
While His Majesty himself does the honours of the
house!

FATHER. (uneasy, seeing the DRUNKARD approach) Now
what does he want?

HENRY. This gentleman is a foreign envoy or else an
ambassador!

FATHER. An ambassador, eh? Whatever you do, don't
make a fool of yourself ... (Aloud) It is indeed a
pleasure, Your Excellency, to welcome you under our
roof.

DRUNKARD. I am both honoured and flattered, Your
Majesty. (He bows down before MOLLY) Permit me,
O loveliest of maidens, to adorn the bosom of your
best man with the flower of my chivalrous homage.

MOLLY. Thank you.

FATHER. It is my sincerest wish, Mr. Ambassador, that
relations between our two powerful governments in
accord with international harmony and co-operation
and with a view to consolidating and safeguarding, as
well as everlasting peace which for centuries has
constituted the guiding principle, and in the interest
of mankind. If you touch me, you pig, I'll clobber you

in the kisser and slap you in irons.

DRUNKARD. The consolidation and safeguarding as well as
mankind in the spirit of co-operation and in the interest
of everlasting peace constitutes the guiding and in-
violable principle of our peaceful aspirations that are
enlivened by the spirit of mutual understanding. I'm
going to touch you, see ... I'm going to blow myself
up, you pig, and lay you out flat ...

FATHER. May I offer you some pastry?

DRUNKARD. That's terribly kind of you. (To HENRY,
aside) Quick! Now's the time! Stick your finger in his
belly!

HENRY. My father?

DRUNKARD. Then afterwards you will be King!

HENRY. (musingly) Me?

(The stage becomes motionless)

I'm only joking, of course ... But what if ... To
overthrow this father and seize power! To be in control
of the situation! To be in control!
Everything keeps slipping away from me! It's terrible!
I am no longer master of the situation! I'm like a
puppet in a puppet show. To control! Oh, if only I had
control!
To govern!
No, no, I was only joking, of course ... But what if I
were to overthrow this King! What do I need him for
anyway? I made him King so he could grant me a
marriage. But why should I let myself be married by
someone else? If I were to become master, I could
grant myself a marriage - and a decent and respectable one too. Then I would be the one who makes
laws. I would be the one who decides what is holy,
what is virtuous, what is a sacrament - I would be the
one who decides everything!
Oh, God! If only I could be in control!

Oh, God! What God? Oh, Father! What father? It was
I who made them what they are. By virtue of my
bounty! By virtue of my will! Why should I kneel down
before them? Why not kneel down before myself,
myself, myself, the sole source of my law?
Shhh! ... Don't say that. Why do you say that?
You're only repeating what he (points to the DRUNK-
ARD) said.

Well so what if he said it? I'll destroy him too!
It is I who create kings!
It is I who should be King!
I am supreme! There is nothing higher than me!
I am God!

And it is my finger, my finger, which ... (Frightened)
No, it isn't true! I didn't mean it! It isn't true! I
wouldn't betray my father for anything in the world!
My King!

(To the DRUNKARD) I shall not betray him!

DRUNKARD. You won't betray him, you pig?

FATHER. (who has been listening) What, what, what? ...
Treason? ...

HENRY. That's not what I wanted to say!

FATHER. Don't you come near me!

HENRY. I'm not coming near you.

FATHER. Don't move! Don't anybody move!

HENRY. I'm not moving. (Despairingly) Why are you afraid
of me?

FATHER. Me? Henry, my son, my child, how could I be
afraid of you, my friend, my defender, my support?
No, no, Henry, I'm not afraid ...

HENRY. Calm yourself ...

FATHER.
　　　　Adjust my sash, oh, oh,
　　　　Adjust my sash ...

HENRY. (adjusting the sash)
　　　　He's trembling, his heart is pounding and his cheeks
　　　　Are bathed with sweat ...

FATHER. (quietly) Tssst ... Henry ...

HENRY. What is it?

FATHER. You'd better go away ... Go away.

HENRY. Why?

FATHER. Henry, why should I be afraid of you? ... Oh,
　　　　perhaps just a little bit, just a tiny bit, maybe just
　　　　a teeny-weeny bit - you know, just in case ... But I
　　　　am the King, Henry, so I think you'd better leave me
　　　　now, because even though it's small, being royal it
　　　　might grow ... it might become gigantic ... and then
　　　　one day it might explode! And the King and me might
　　　　get carried away!

HENRY. Calm down ... Control yourself ...

FATHER. How can I control myself if I am ... greater
　　　　than myself?

HENRY. Shhh! ... Don't shout!

FATHER.
　　　　I'm not shouting

　　　　It's my voice which is shouting! Tssst ... (In a
　　　　loud voice) Thank you, my son, for your loyalty! I
　　　　know in your filial heart there isn't any treason. No,
　　　　there isn't any! I haven't the slightest bit of doubt. Not
　　　　the slightest ... and if I say I haven't any doubts, it's
　　　　not because

　　　　I have any; and I emphasize

That I say it not because of that, it's just
So nobody will think I'm coming back to it

For some other reason. But what I just got through
explaining should likewise not be interpreted as a
sign of

My distrust. (To the DIGNITARIES) Stop
Listening to me! Why
Do you listen to me all the time? Why

Don't you stop gawping at me? Do you think it's very
pleasant to be listened to and gawped at all the time?
Get out of here, out, out!

No, no, stay here! I
Have nothing to hide. If I tell you
To get out, it does not mean at all

that I have something to hide. No, no, I don't have
any doubts as far as my son is concerned; I am pos-
itive he is not a traitor, I have no doubts whatsoever,
none whatsoever ... For if I had even the slightest
bit of doubt in this respect, even so much as the slightest
then this tiny grain of doubt would in the presence of so
many, many people and the expectation of so many,
many people ... this doubt, I say, this tiny, insig-
nificant doubt ... would become larger ... just a
tiny bit larger ... and that larger doubt would provoke
a light trembling which, being a royal trembling,
would provoke a great panic ... and then an even
greater one ... greater than me even ... and that
panic would carry me away, because the King is
carrying me away! And if the King trembles, I cannot
stop him from trembling! And if the King shouts, I
cannot make him lower his voice! And the King, the
King, the King is shouting: treason! Treason! Treason!

COURT. Treason!

HENRY. Treason!

FATHER.
        Help! Guards! Guards!

92

(The GUARDS rush in)

> He has a finger!
> Oh, treason, treason, treason!

HENRY. (touching the FATHER with his finger)
> Arrest
> Arrest this father of mine! And cast him
> Into some dark and dreary,
> Foul and oppressive
> Godforsaken dungeon!
> (Despairingly) That's not what I wanted to say!

DRUNKARD. (with delight) He toushhed him! He toushhed him in the belly! (He makes as though is is going to attack the FATHER)

HENRY. (to JOHNNY, indicating the DRUNKARD)
> Arrest
> This pig! And into the dungeon with him!
> (To everyone) I don't know how it happened
> But it happened! I betrayed
> My father!
> (To the DRUNKARD) What time is it?

DRUNKARD. Seven.

FATHER. (groaning)
> Henreee ...

COURT. (thunderously)
> Oh, Henry!

HENRY. (thunderously)
> Oh, Henry!
> Now I am King!
> Bind him, break his bones and trample him under-
>   foot!

(The GUARDS arrest the FATHER)

MOTHER. (in a shrill voice) Henry, dear, what are you doing?

HENRY.

Now I shall rule! I alone!

I shall get married on my own! And nobody is going to
stand in my way! I've just had the old man placed under
arrest. That drunkard has likewise been taken into custody. Now I am King, now I am the one who is in control, now I shall get married on my own ...

Enough of this idle chatter! Do you think
That I am blind? That I don't see

How you're trying to make a chump out of me? But
that's all over now. I'm not going to dance to your
tune any more. I'm not going to be your puppet on a
string. I'll force you to obey and respect my will. If
the old man's afraid to rule, if he's unable to marry
me, I'll get married by myself. Where is my fiancee?
(Seeing MOLLY approach)

Ah, here she comes. She has ceased to be pure
But don't worry, I shall purify her! I shall lead her
    out of here!
I shall grant myself a marriage! I alone!
Let nobody try to interfere! I shall do it myself!
Because I am alone here, I am alone here
And none of you are here!

(Procession. HENRY and MOLLY lead. Wedding
march)

I am marching at the head ... What do I care
If the others are trailing behind me like a tail
I cannot see them. I am passing
Through pure space, an empty void ...

(Noticing the DRUNKARD who is being guarded by
JOHNNY)

And get that imbecile out of here, eliminate him ...
Do away with him ... you won't get off very easily
with me ... Sentence him to death!

94

DRUNKARD. (in the voice of a beggar) Master ... Master
...

HENRY. That sounded pretty silly, didn't it? ... Well,
you won't be doing me any more harm where you're
going!

DRUNKARD. You Majesty! Ah, what's the use! So much
the worse for me! Very well. So be it then! (To everyone) They're going to hang me, they're going to hang
me! That's all they've been doing around here for the
last few years - hanging people! (To HENRY) Sire,
I have but one request to make before I die. That I
might be permitted to have one last look at her.

HENRY. Who?

DRUNKARD. My Queen.

HENRY. I bet he's up to another one of his tricks. But I
am not afraid any more - everything is dependent on
my will now.

All right, go ahead.
You're looking at her.

DRUNKARD. (to himself) Oh, Molly, Molly - would I like
to have a slug of you!

HENRY. (to himself) Ha, ha, ha!

DRUNKARD. I didn't marry you, and now it's someone
else's turn.

HENRY. Let him say whatever he pleases. (To JOHNNY)
Keep a close watch on him.

DRUNKARD. If I didn't have this joker on my back, if I
hadn't been arrested - I'd've known how to ... with
you, me, me and you ...

HENRY. He's talking gibberish.

DRUNKARD. I shall carry the image of your angelic face
with me always unto the four walls of my coffin, and
there with your image before me I shall turn up my
toes ... hic ... (To HENRY) Sir, I beseech you to
grant me this one last favour - ask this young fellow
here (points to JOHNNY) to take a flower out of that
vase and hold it a little bit above Her Majesty's
precious little head while I stand over here and watch.

HENRY. This is another of his idiotic pranks, but if I
refuse everyone will get the idea I'm afraid ... so
I'd better not refuse. (To JOHNNY) Do as he says.
(To MOLLY) My dearest Mary, I trust you will see
it in your heart to grant this pathetic maniac his last
dying wish.

DRUNKARD. Oh, my Queen! My only wish is to die with
your image before my eyes ... I humbly entreat you
to hold the flower jus' a little bit lower ... so it
barely comes down over her eyes ... (While lowering
the flower, JOHNNY embraces MARY) Now just a
little bit lower ... that's it, that's it ... Oh, my
Queen!

HENRY. What's he trying to prove? It doesn't mean a
thing.

DIGNITARIES. (waking up, theatrically)
It doesn't mean a thing
It's quite harmless!
Poor soul!
It's rather amusing.

DRUNKARD. Excuse me, jus' a little bit lower ... so the
flower barely touches her neck ... Oh, that's it,
that's it, perfect.... Oh, how ravishing ...

DIGNITARIES.
One must admire the patience of His Majesty.
Not only is he just but he's generous too.
One must admire the patience of Her Majesty
Her Majesty is exceedingly generous!

96

DRUNKARD. (unexpectedly, gravely) And now don't either
of you move, 'cos I'm going to take away the flower.
(He pulls the flower out of JOHNNY's hand) Don't
move ...

MOLLY. This is just like posing for a photograph.

HENRY. (to JOHNNY and MOLLY) Wait a second. (To
himself) Well, so what? (To JOHNNY) Don't move.
(To himself) I wonder what he's up to?

This is absurd. I thought he was more clever ...

DRUNKARD. Clever.

HENRY. Clever?

DRUNKARD. Clever ...

HENRY. What do you mean, clever? What's so clever
about that? The flower's already been discarded and
they're still standing in the same artificial position
... Clever?

DRUNKARD. Clever ...

HENRY. Clever?

What of it? They're standing there together ... So?
They're standing together ...
Ah, the two of them together ... He with her, and
she
With him ... Well, so what if they are? Together
But it doesn't make any sense ... They're standing
there in an artificial manner. Wait a minute ...
Well, what of it? ... They're standing there, and
the rest of us
Are looking on ... While they go on standing there
...
You pig!
You've bound them together
By a dreadful
And inferior bond. You've married them

97

You pig priest!

DRUNKARD. You pig!

HENRY. You pig!

(laughter of the DIGNITARIES)

ACT THREE

(A hall in the castle; HENRY and the CHANCELLOR)

CHANCELLOR. There is peace. All the rebellious elements
are under arrest. Assembly has also been taken into
custody along with military and civilian circles, vast
segments of the population, the High Court, the Joint
Chiefs of Staff, Boards and Departments, all public
and private authorities, the press, hospitals and
orphanages. All the Ministries have been placed
under arrest, and everything else besides; in short,
Your Majesty - everything. The police have likewise
been imprisoned. There is peace. Quiet. It's humid.

HENRY. Indeed. There is peace. How calm it is.

CHANCELLOR. Well, what did you expect? It's autumn.

HENRY. Where is the Chief of Police?

CHANCELLOR. He's waiting.

HENRY. Well, as long as he's waiting, let him wait. And
what about my father, the ex-King?

CHANCELLOR. Under arrest.

HENRY. And that ... drunkard?

CHANCELLOR. Under arrest.

HENRY. (gloomily, bitterly) Today's the wedding ... What
a miserable day!

CHANCELLOR. A day like any other.

HENRY. You're getting old.

CHANCELLOR. I'm afraid so.

HENRY.
I am in power.
Never mind how I came by it. I took control
Of the situation ... and so everything will be
As I command ... Therefore I command
Everyone to assemble here, in this hall, because
  the King has decided
To bestow a marriage on himself.
Now take those louts by the snouts and drag them
  in here!

CHANCELLOR. Yes, Your Majesty.

HENRY. Have my father brought in under heavy guard. By
the snout. I wish to get married in his presence.

CHANCELLOR. Yes, Your Majesty.

HENRY. And have my mother brought in, too. By the
snout.

CHANCELLOR. Yes, Your Majesty.

HENRY. And that drunkard too ... but securely bound,
mind you. I want everyone to be present when I ad-
minister the sacrament to myself. I'm not afraid of
anybody. Nobody can do me any harm. I alone know
what I must do, and that's that. I am in command now
and so everything will be done according to my will.
I am in control; I am in control of the situation. If
anybody conspires against me or tries to commit
acts of sabotage, take the lout by the snout and ...
Has the Chief of Police arrived with his henchmen?
Show them in.

(Enter the CHIEF OF POLICE and three of his
HENCHMEN)

HENRY. Just what I needed! Look at these snouts! Ho, ho,

these snouts will take them by the snouts! Yes sir! If anybody gets out of line or in any way tries to interfere or cause trouble, take the lout by the snout and slap him silly in front of everybody ... for all to see ...

CHANCELLOR. I'm afraid, Sire, that ... Let's see, what was it I wanted to say?

HENRY. My head is clear. Listen to my way of reasoning. Please, listen to my way of reasoning. I have already lost my innocence. They robbed me of my virginity. Lately, though, I've been doing a lot of thinking on my own. I didn't sleep a wink last night!
Holiness, majesty, power, law, morality, love, ridiculousness, stupidity, wisdom - all these come from people in the same way that wine comes from grapes. Like wine, understand? I have the situation well in hand and I shall force these apes to produce everything my heart desires. And if that is ridiculous, I'll take that ridiculousness by the snout too! And if that is foolish, I'll take that foolishness by the snout too! And if God, old antediluvian God, has anything against it, I'll take him by the snout too! ...

CHANCELLOR and CHIEF. Yes, Your Majesty!

HENCHMEN. Yes, Your Majesty!

HENRY. Yes, Your Majesty!

ALL. Yes, Your Majesty!

(Enter PANDULF)

PANDULF. No!

HENRY. No?

PANDULF. No!

HENRY. Well, I'll be d ... If it isn't the Bishop!

PANDULF.

> I am Pandulf.
> A cardinal of the Roman Catholic Church, and I
>   declare this
> To your face, you infamous usurper: God exists
> And a marriage not consecrated by the Church
> Is not a marriage, but a sacrilege!

HENRY.

> Ha, ha, ha, Pandulf, Pandulf!

PANDULF.

> Yes, I am Pandulf.

HENRY.

> Ah ... and you're
> A cardinal too, if I'm not mistaken? ...

PANDULF.

> I am a servant of God
> A servant of God, I, Pandulf ...

HENRY.

> My dear Pandulf, you aren't by any chance ... a
>   little tipsy
> Tipsy
> Tipsy
> With this Pandulf of yours? Well? My dear Pandulf,
>   you aren't a little bit tight
> Tight
> Tight
> With the cardinal of yours? The cardinal has gone
>   to your head. Booze
> Booze
> Booze

But my dear Pandulf, you are absolutely blind drunk
with your Lord God and the Holy Catholic Church.
You're nothing but an ordinary drunkard, Pandulf.
Shame on you! Oh, I know all about it. First one glass,
then another, pretty soon - away you go! No Pandulf,
you're no ordinary fellow. You're a drunkard!

PANDULF.
   I curse
   You!

HENRY. What? Are you taking nips again? Are you getting
   pickled on your own curse in my presence? Well, this
   has gone far enough. I'm going to touch you. (He touches
   him)

PANDULF. Oh, God ...

HENRY.
   Arrest this boozy priest!
   Arrest him. Come on, henchmen,
   Take him by the snout!

   (PANDULF is whisked offstage by the HENCHMEN)

   What a miserable day!

CHANCELLOR. Yes, it's a miserable day ...

HENRY. I am ruling ...

CHANCELLOR. Yes, Your Majesty.

HENRY. I shall rule ...

CHANCELLOR. Yes, Your Majesty.

HENRY. I'm going to touch everybody.

CHANCELLOR. Yes, Your Majesty.

HENRY.
   No one will dare to touch me ... By the way,
   My dear Chancellor,
   Tell me, people aren't by any chance making fun
     of me a little
   Are they? ...

CHANCELLOR. Oh, oh, oh!

CHIEF. Oh, oh, oh!

HENRY.
> They aren't saying
> Behind my back somewhere, and
> Behind their own backs too, that ... that ... that ...
> That I'm jealous, for example, ha, ha! Well,
>   are they? That would be
> A laugh, wouldn't it?

CHANCELLOR. Oh, oh, oh!

CHIEF. Oh, oh, oh!

HENRY.
> I only ask
> On account of that silly little episode
> With the flower, ha, ha, ha! The insinuation
> Made by that contemptible drunkard left little
>   room for doubt
> And may have given more fodder
> To these foul and slippery tongues, ha, ha, ha!

CHANCELLOR. I know nothing about it!

CHIEF. We know nothing about it!

HENRY.
> Because
> If he connected them in such a singular position
> Then they are connected ... and perhaps others
> Are likewise connecting them ... her with him, and
>   him
> With her ... Well? Speak up! Perhaps
> No one will have the nerve to say it openly
> But that won't stop them from smirking, insinuating,
>   or winking with one eye,
> Exchanging meaningful glances or signalling on the
>   sly, ha, ha, ha ...

My throat is dry. My throat has gone dry. Hey,
servant, bring me an apple! I'm going to have an
apple! (To the CHANCELLOR) Well? Well?

106

CHANCELLOR. Properly speaking, Your Majesty, everyone
is acting properly, but then again, properly speaking,
perhaps improperly too, who knows; perhaps people
are insinuating things, and then again, maybe they
aren't, how should I know, I'm nearsighted, my vision
isn't what it used to be ...

HENRY. You blind old nag! You blind old mole!

CHIEF. I'm nearsighted too.

HENRY. I'll let the air out of both of you ... (To the
SERVANT who has brought the apple) Wait a moment.
Stand still, let me get a good look at you. Who knows
what this man might be

    Thinking

In private, up there ... Look at him! He's a numskull,
one of those shady types. But who knows? Perhaps

    He's imagining something. Perhaps in his mind
    He's connecting ...
    He's connecting the two of them there ...
    Perhaps he's making fun of me in private
    And betraying me ... with him ... and with her ...
    Oh, the traitors!

They're betraying me! They're nothing but a bunch of
traitors! And this immobile face. How do I know but
at this very moment he isn't laughing at me or insinuating something awful, whether inwardly he isn't
howling with laughter ... This apple is lying between
my knife and fork. Knife and fork. What's it doing
between my knife and fork? Oh, yes, of course, that's
how they always serve apples, peaches, pears ...
No, besides it's absurd. There was never anything
between Johnny and her ... No, it's just my imagination ... I know it's idiotic and yet

    I have to say it ... and saying it
    I declare it ...

CHANCELLOR. (to the CHIEF)
>   His Majesty
>   Is curiously absorbed with his thoughts ...

CHIEF.
>   He's probably
>   Troubled by unwholesome dreams.

HENRY. (to himself)
>   I don't want to drink any more
>   I'm not going to drink any more ...

CHANCELLOR. (aside)
>   Tch, tch, tch, vodka, vodka!

HENRY. (to himself)
>   Until now perhaps
>   There has never been anything between them, but
>   now
>   That everybody connects them, maybe he connects
>   himself
>   With her too ... And connecting himself with her
>   Touches her ...

CHANCELLOR.
>   Oh, oh, oh, vodka, vodka ...

HENRY. (to himself)
>   I hear what I'm saying
>   And I hear what he's saying. And I know perfectly
>   well
>   That what we're both saying is pure comedy
>   All the same, I must speak ...

CHANCELLOR. (delightedly, aloud)
>   The king is sozzled!

HENRY. (to the CHANCELLOR) Shut your trap! (He slaps
>   the CHIEF OF POLICE in the face)

CHIEF. Why me?

HENRY.
>   Just to keep you guessing! At the moment

I am in need of a little brutality - and I'm searching
for it

In your face! If I'd struck the Chancellor, I would
have been acting only justly. But I want to be brutal!
I'm going to establish order here! (Cries are heard)
Now what's the matter?

MOTHER. (offstage)
    Let go of me, let go!
    (She bursts in)
    Oh, Henry, my little Henry, your father, your
        father, your father!

HENRY. Has she gone mad?

MOTHER.
    Oh, Henry, your father's yelling, your father's
        screaming
    Ranting and raving like an animal, jumping up
    And down!

HENRY. He must have gone crazy!

MOTHER. (dramatically, lyrically)
    He tried to break loose, he tried to escape
    Far, far away, into the hills
    But they caught 'im
    And now they're whippin' his ass
    Oh, Henry, he's a pain in your ass!

HENRY. So? What's that got to do with me?

MOTHER.
    Oh, a knife, a knife, a knife!

HENRY. I hold my knife this way.

MOTHER. (terrified)
    For God's sake, Henry!
    I'm your mother!

HENRY. That's right - you are my mother. What a happy

coincidence ... (He walks up to her) I'd like to hug you and kiss you, mamma ... (He puts his arms around her)

MOTHER. Henry, what are you doing?

HENRY. I'm hugging you.

MOTHER.
You'd better leave me alone
There's something odd about the way you hug me
No, no, leave me in peace!

CHANCELLOR. That's odd, that's odd ...

CHIEF. Odd, positively distasteful ...

(FATHER bursts in, followed by the HENCHMEN)

FATHER. Help! They're beating me!

MOTHER. Murderers!

FATHER. (quietly)
They beat me
(Louder) They beat me
(Shouting) They beat me! Me! Me!

MOTHER. Come here, he beat me too.

FATHER. (shouting) What? What? Has he been beating you?

MOTHER. Quiet, quiet, shh ...

FATHER. (in a lower voice) Just for that I'll curse the son-of-a ...

MOTHER. Shh! Shh!

FATHER. What? What was that you said? He hit you?

HENRY. Lucky thing I have this knife ...

ALL. Oh!

HENRY.
    No, what an idea! I'm not going to kill anyone,
      even though this knife
    Is sharpening me!
    I'm not going to kill anyone - I'm merely going
    To touch them ...
    (He touches his MOTHER and FATHER)
    O cruel and abominable couple
    Who would their own son curse! Father and mother!
      Holy of holies! But
    I am touching them
    Look how I'm touching them, look how I'm moving
      them, look how I'm digging into their gut!

CHANCELLOR.
    Never before
    Have my poor old eyes
    Seen such a sight ...

CHIEF.
    Never in a million years
    Would I have imagined anything like this!

A HENCHMAN. What a disgrace!

FATHER. May you perish!

MOTHER. Would that your mother had suffered a mis-
    carriage!

FATHER. May your father strangle you to death!

MOTHER. May you never have any children!

FATHER. May your children turn you out in your old age!

MOTHER. May they strangle you to death!

FATHER. May they pluck out your eyes!

HENRY.
>Take them away!
>They're drunk, drunk on motherhood and father-
>>hood!
>But I am sober!

(The HENCHMEN converge upon the MOTHER AND
FATHER)

FATHER.
>Henreee ...

HENRY. What is it?

FATHER.
>Henre-e-e

>Henr-r-r, Henr-e-e-e, I realize you've taken the King
>away from me ... but I'm still your father after all
>... For God's sake, Henry, don't deprive me of the
>father, because if you do, the universe will burst into
>smithereens with such an earsplitting, god-awful
>racket ...

HENRY. Father is a title the same as King is. Can't you
speak like an ordinary man? Must you always get
dressed up in some title or other?

>I feel sleepy. Take them away!

FATHER.
>With these words
>You open the gates to a terrible misfortune
>Oh, Lord

MOTHER. Have mercy ...

CHANCELLOR. On us sinners ... (He pulls a newspaper
out of his pocket) War has been declared!

HENRY. What? What war?

CHANCELLOR.
>I received this newspaper

Only a moment ago.

(Silence. In the distance, sounds of a cannon exploding)

HENRY. It's true - they're shooting.

FATHER. It sounds like it's coming from the forest ...

(General anxiety)

MOTHER. We'd better start packing.

CHANCELLOR. If necessary we can go down into the basement.

FATHER. Artillery is nothing. The worst is poison gas. We'd better stock up on supplies ... (To MOTHER) Go out and buy whatever you can - the stores will be closed soon.

MOTHER. I've got some gas masks around here somewhere ... but where? I've got them somewhere, but I can't remember ... which drawer it was ... (With growing uneasiness) Where have I been keeping them?

(An explosion)

CHIEF. It's getting closer.

CHANCELLOR.
        Sire, will you give
        The orders?

HENRY. I'm not giving any orders, because none of this is real!

        It isn't real! But it is real!
        (Straining his ear)
        Oh, listen to them fight!

FATHER. What'll become of us? What'll become of us now? Oh, misfortune, conflagration, rape, torture, infamy, dishonour ...

HENRY.

That's a lot of rubbish! Just some sort
Of drunken ravings! They're both reeking
With liquor! Throw them out!

FATHER. (drunk)

Hic! ... I'm drunk ... Hic! ... So be it then
My son has said so ... Well, such is life ...
But seeing as I'm already a little tight, then before
   you stick me in the
Dungeon, what do you say me and you have a little
Snort, eh? I'm going to let you in on a little secret!
  I'm going to whishper something in your ear
That'll go straight to your head ...

MOTHER. (drunk) Tra-la-la ...

FATHER.

Don't marry that girl!
That old drunk was telling you the truth. She
Used to whore around with your friend Johnny.

HENRY. That's a lie!

FATHER.

I'm telling you the truth!

I didn't want to tell you before because I was too
ashamed, but seeing as everything has gone to hell
anyway ...

On the very same day
You and she got engaged, I
Caught 'em in the bushes, stumbled across 'em
  them in the bushes,
And stepped on 'em with my foot!

HENRY.

It isn't true!
And yet it is true!

MOTHER.

I caught 'em too once
Snuggled up together by the well

114

They were playin' footsie with each other
Right there in broad daylight! Don't marry that
  girl, Henry!

(Sound of an explosion)

HENRY. They've started up again!

FATHER. (looking out the window) Soldiers.

CHANCELLOR. Soldiers.

MOTHER. They're just kids. Wet behind the ears.

FATHER. Maybe so, but they're already bleeding.

MOTHER.
  Henry, don't you marry that girl!
  She used to smile at the younger ones too
  She used to fool around with the younger ones too!

FATHER.
  She bled a lot
  With men younger than she!

MOTHER.
  In the bushes
  Under some tree, or in the hay ...

FATHER. In the cellar!

MOTHER. Or in the attic!

FATHER. In the barn!

MOTHER. Or in the coach house!

FATHER.
  In her panties
  Or without her panties!
  (Gazing out the window) Ohh,
  look how they're strangling that guy,
  Look how they're mashing him ... Now

They sticking him with a bayonet!

MOTHER. O ruin and conflagration!

FATHER. We'd better cover the window with something
- if they spot us, they might come in here after us.

HENRY.
You degenerate old
Flea-bitten boozer,
And you, you rickety, old,
Whisky-guzzling floozy ... I've been far too
Lenient
And far too patient
With your rotgut ravings! But now
You will know my wrath! Out! Out! Out! I am alone!
Lock them in irons!

(The MOTHER and FATHER are taken away by the
HENCHMEN)

FATHER. Have mercy on us!

HENRY. I shall grant this marriage myself! I shall marry
her, I'll get married on my own! The rest is nothing
but the foulmouthed ravings of some drunken fools!
Blah-blah, blah! Bring my fiancee in here at once!
It's time we began discussing the details of our nuptial
ceremony. But first ...

CHANCELLOR. But first. ...

HENRY. But first ...

CHANCELLOR. But first ...

HENRY. But first ...
Summon my courtier this ... what's his name ...
John ... that's it ... John, my courtier ... I must
have a few words with him ... and with her ...

(All exeunt)

... and now we'll find out if there's anything between them ... and if there is ...

(Enter JOHNNY)

.. we'll settle the matter once and for all. (To JOHNNY) Oh, it's you, Johnny. How are you getting along?

JOHNNY. Not bad.

HENRY. Not bad, not bad and not bad with me either! Johnny, I'm afraid we've become involved in some ... not altogether pleasant affair ...

JOHNNY. I don't care. It's better than being in the army.

HENRY. What time is it?

JOHNNY. Five-thirty.

HENRY. Where did you get that watch?

JOHNNY. I bought in in Antwerp.

HENRY. What's going on there? I understand war has been declared.

JOHNNY. So I've heard.

HENRY. But you don't know for certain.

JOHNNY. Can anything be known for certain? You know, Henry, if I were you I wouldn't believe a word anyone says around here ... There's something false and pretentious about everything here ...

HENRY. You're right, Johnny, nothing is real around here ... Everyone pretends to be himself and lies in order to tell the truth ... It's even a little amusing, if you ask me ... But I've already got used to it. And what about yourself, Johnny ... are you a little ... hm ... tight too?

JOHNNY. Me?

HENRY. Everyone around here is getting drunk on something different. And so I thought perhaps you'd been ... drinking something too.

JOHNNY. No.

HENRY. Well, then why do you look so sad?

JOHNNY. Me? I'm not sad at all. Quite the contrary.

HENRY. (sadly) In appearance you aren't, but all the same you are ... and your sadness is lurking in the shadows ... Hallo, hallo, come on out here, come on out here!

(MOLLY emerges from the shadows)

What's new?

MOLLY. Nothing.

HENRY. How have you been?

MOLLY. All right.

HENRY. I have something to tell you ... both of you ... You won't believe it but ever since that drunkard joined you together with the flower, ha, ha, ha, in such a peculiar position, into a statue, ha, ha, ha, I can't get rid of the impression that there's something between you two ... that something's going on between you two ... ha, ha, ha!

    Ha, ha, ha!
    Ha, ha, ha!
    Well, how do I know!

JOHNNY. What's that supposed to mean? That you're jealous?

HENRY. You're speaking to me, but for whom are you speaking?

JOHNNY. I don't understand.

HENRY. You're standing there as if you were alone - but with <u>whom</u> are you standing? (To MOLLY) Why don't you look at him?

MOLLY. Why should I?

HENRY. Even if you don't look at him, it's <u>him</u> you're not looking at.

MOLLY. (theatrically) Henry, I love you!

HENRY. Yes, you love me, and he is my friend. You love me and you're a respectable girl ... but what have you been serving? (To JOHNNY) And what have you been serving?

JOHNNY. What do you mean?

HENRY. Haven't you been serving evil? You have more crimes on your conscience than a common criminal. You are both respectable people, you are both innocent, you both come from a good home ... but what have you been serving? So now

> You serve her, and let
> Her serve you!

MOLLY. (theatrically) Oh, don't torture me like this!

HENRY. Both you and he love me ... but only when <u>each of you is alone!</u> But the two of you ... but the two <u>of you together</u> ... Together you are altogether different from what you are separately!

JOHNNY. The two of us together are nothing, so stop persecuting us as well as yourself!

HENRY. Us! Us! Why do you say "us"? Ah, what strange things go on in this world of ours!
Imagine - after he threw away that flower, it suddenly became apparent that you were together ... you must

119

have been aware of that yourselves ... And now everyone is joining you together, and I am likewise joining
you together ... in my mind, of course ... and you
are becoming more and more intimately connected!
Oh, in some strange, inexplicable way that man has
joined you together in wedlock! He must be a priest!
An unholy priest of some mysterious rite ... A
psychological priest!

JOHNNY. What's happening to you? You're all excited.

HENRY. Am I? I'm beginning to doubt whether I exist
at all. It seems to me that I feel, that I think, that
I make decisions ... but in reality nothing is decided
inside me; everything is decided between ... between
ourselves ... It's between ourselves that spring the
forces, the charms, the gods, the illusions which toss
us about like straws in the wind ... And we flounder
along ... ;

JOHNNY. How so?

HENRY. Look what happened to me, for instance. He joined
you together in a certain way, stacked you one of top
of the other, multiplied you one times the other - or
again, he attached you to her and her to you - and made
out of you something which excites me ... which in-
toxicates me to such an extent that (menacingly) I
shall not rest until I have married her. Remember
that.

JOHNNY. I won't stand in your way.

HENRY. Oh, why has my nature brought me to this? Why
after such a cloudy ... cloudy ... voyage have I put
in to such a port? How is such a phenomenon to be
explained? Perhaps secretly I harbour a certain
affection for you - an inarticulate, illicit, amoral and
abnormal affection.

JOHNNY. Whatever that's supposed to mean.

HENRY. Perhaps subconsciously I have been jealous about
her all along ... and of you ... and regarded you all

along as my rival?

JOHNNY. So what?

HENRY. All the same, who knows whether it is possible ...
whether in general it is possible for a man to fall in
love with a woman without the co-operation, without the
intermediary of another man? It may be that in
general man is incapable of responding to a woman
except through the intermediary of another man.
Might this not be some new form of love? Before,
only two were needed, but today it's three.

JOHNNY. I think you're exaggerating.

HENRY. Perhaps this is something which has been imposed
on me from without; perhaps deep down inside I don't
feel that way at all, but merely feel obliged to behave
as though in fact I did. My head is spinning from
this winding, tortuous road down which I keep walking,
and walking ... endlessly ... without a moment's rest
... Oh, heavy are these gates, oppressive is this
ceiling, strange and enigmatic is this sky.
Oh, that drunkard has made me drunk. Oh, that
priest really is a priest. With his finger ... with his
finger ... he has fashioned an idol out of you ... before
which I must kneel and offer sacrifice as in a dream.

> The hell I will!
> I am still the King! It is I who rule!
> I shall rule! Oh, Henry, Henry, Henry! I am alone!
> I shall confer this marriage myself! Henry!
> Don't let yourself be ruled! You be the one who rules!
> Henry, cast down these gods, destroy these spells
> And your own throne ascend!

How strange that sounded. Damn it! If only I didn't
have to speak in such an artificial manner. And here
she is ... standing right beside us ... and listening.

MOLLY. (theatrically) Why do you torture yourself and
me so!

HENRY. What an insufferable ham! There are times when
I'd like to ... (Makes a gesture as though he is
about to strike her)

MOLLY. (in a vulgar tone) Hey, you needn't try any of
that on me, mister!

HENRY.
Leave me.
I have to talk with him in private.
Don't go too far away though. Have
The servants bring you some tea.

(MOLLY goes out)

And now
Let's get down to business. I only wish I knew
    the outcome of all this.
What a dreadful silence ...
These walls and everything around here is waiting
    patiently to hear
What I am going to say.

It's been a long time since I've felt so jumpy. (To
JOHNNY) Ah, Johnny, how's it going?

JOHNNY. All right.

HENRY. I'd like to have a few words with you. Sit down.

JOHNNY. All right.

HENRY.
I have something unpleasant to tell you
Something which may even be a little abnormal
In the sense that it's not altogether common or usual
But departs rather from the normal couse of events.

JOHNNY.
What do I care if something's abnormal
As long as I am normal!

HENRY.
The point is if I told you in an ordinary manner

122

It would not be convincing. Everything depends
On how we speak. That is why
I have to tell you this in a manner which is perhaps
   a trifle
Artificial.

And I must ask you on your part not to respond to me
in a normal manner, but to conduct yourself exactly as
I tell you. No one will be coming in here. We'll lock
the door.

JOHNNY. Do whatever you like.

HENRY. I know. You've already been forced to do so many
   strange things in spite of your youth. But I assure
   you this is not a caprice of mine, but something far
   more serious. As you know, my dear Johnny, I have
   deposed my father, the King, and ascended the throne
   myself. And today I have decided to grant myself a
   marriage to my fiancee, Princess Mary. Say: Yes, I
   know.

JOHNNY. Yes, I know.

HENRY. But what's the sense of marrying her, even in the
   most formal manner, if the whole Court believes you
   and she are enjoying some sort of intimate relations
   .. and if I myself, rightly or wrongly, imagine that
   you and she ... Say: Yes.

JOHNNY. All right, if it'll make you happier: Yes.

HENRY. No, no, say "yes" without any commentary.
   Honestly, nobody is listening to us ... although we are
   listening to ourselves ... Say: Yes.

JOHNNY. Yes.

HENRY. Of course, it would be quite simple for me to ...
   to do away with you ... to arrest you as I did with
   that drunkard. I could even liquidate you, kill you,
   let's say. But even if I did, it wouldn't change a thing,
   because ... because I would always be left with the

foreboding suspicion that she really belonged to you
and not to me. Say: Yes.

JOHNNY. Yes.

HENRY. These curtains are impossible. I don't understand
why this palace is so shabby and poorly kept. There
are so many servants around here and still the dirt
is everywhere. I have to do something about that.
Don't say anything. I'm not finished.
What do you think of me?

JOHNNY. I think you're sick.

HENRY. I'll explain a few things to you, as far as they
can be explained.
Every since I became involved in all this, I've been
wavering between two poles: between responsibility
and irresponsibility, between truth and falsity. On the
one hand, I'm convinced that what is going on here is
unreal, irresponsible, artificial, cheap ... On the
other hand, I take all this very seriously and feel as
though I bear final responsibility for everything.

I can't refrain from using artificial phrases.

But at the same time these phrases appear less artificial to me than simplicity itself.

I know I am not a real king.
And yet I feel like a king.
I'm enjoying every minute of it.

But at the very same time I know this game is not
quite so innocent as it seems. I feel as if, when I
pretend something, I actually bring that something
into existence, as though with my every word and
deed I conjure up and create something ... something
far more powerful than myself.
What do you think of that?

JOHNNY. It's pretty vague.

HENRY. Yes, but you behave at times as though you knew

124

something about it - and so do the others ... What do
you know? Do you know more or less than I do?
No, I haven't gone crazy. I am a clear-thinking, modern man. Why do I really wish to marry her? Because
I'd like to have her as she was before - and I know
and I am convinced that if I possessed her without
marrying her, I would not be possessing my former
fiancee but some worn-out, broken-down slut ... I
would like this marriage which I'm bestowing upon
myself and her to be truly sacred. Does that sound
like the idea of a mystic or that of a madman? Or am
I incapable of such a sacred act? In the last instance,
what is really crucial here? Other people. If others
acknowledge the sacredness of that act, then it will
be sacred - sacred for them. If they acknowledge her
as my chaste and noble Queen, then she will become
a queen - for them. And if she's a queen for them, then
she's a queen for me.

JOHNNY. Your ideas are sound, but you're making a funny
impression on me.

HENRY. Wait a moment. I don't have the power to erase
from her past ... the fact that she was once a whore
in some dive ... and that she once kept company with a
lot of drunkards. But if I force everyone, including
myself, to accept this solemn marriage which at the
same time will have the effect of sanctifying both my
love and her honour - then it will be accepted as such.
For everything is decided between people! Everything
comes from people!

And now listen
But listen carefully: as you know, in a moment
I shall carry out this act ... I am in need of strength
But you are weakening me ...

JOHNNY. Aha.

HENRY. I'll explain my plan of action to you. It's an extremely simple and even dull plan.
I have given orders for everyone to attend a ball at
the Royal Court. At this ball, with the help of glances,

laughter, caresses, etc.... Molly and I will generate
between ourselves the greatest amount of love possible.
Between ourselves we shall create that love, purity,
and fidelity ... which once existed between us. At the
very same time I shall force this pack of fools to
pump me full of divinity through tokens of respect
and admiration - and then I shall very calmly confer a
marriage upon myself and her which will legalize and
sanctify everything.... What's so strange about that?

Nothing.

Nothing. But you understand that first of all I must
conquer that which is engendered between you ... and
that which weakens me ... I am in need of strength.

But you are depriving me of it ...
And now I shall tell you something
Quite unexpected: you will be obliged
To kill yourself - and the only reason
For that is: I command you to do it
And it is my will ...

JOHNNY. What a nice proposition!

HENRY. I realize it's a little ... silly ... Do you suppose
I'm not ashamed? This is horribly artificial. But I'm
only saying it ... by way of a little experiment ... I'm
merely curious to see how it sounds - understand?
Obviously

You shouldn't take any of this in earnest
Who in his right mind, after all, would take it
  seriously!

It's just that I would like to hear the sound of my own
voice, that's all. But I'd also like to hear how what
you are going to say sounds. Therefore I'll ask you to

Bow your head and bend your arms and legs, crouch
  down a little
And say: If that is your will, Henry, then yes, I'd
  be glad to.

126

JOHNNY. I'm not an actor.

HENRY. Imagine you're learning a poem by heart.

JOHNNY. I don't want to imagine anything.

HENRY. Imagine you're a priest pronouncing the words to some sort of incantation.

JOHNNY. I don't want to imagine anything.

HENRY. Don't you think that a thousand years from now people will speaking to one another in a completely different fashion from the way we do today?

JOHNNY. That's very possible.

HENRY. And that their conversations will be infinitely richer? There are many melodies which our songbook of today does not contain. What harm can it possibly do you to utter these words by way of a little experiment? And to bow your head?

JOHNNY. What good will it do you if I recite them? Words are not facts.

HENRY. O course not. No, no, don't think for a moment that I believe in any kind of magical incantations. I am a modern mind. But what harm can it do you to say that ... and to see how you'll feel while saying it? I'd just like you to get a little taste, a little sample of yourself while you're saying it ... so you can see what it's like ... To a certain extent it can even be thought of in scientific terms. Words evoke certain psychic states in us ... they create worlds of reality between us ... If you said something similar to that ... something strange ... then I could say something even stranger and then, by mutually assisting one another, we could go on and on. So you see - it's not quite as difficult or as absurd as it seemed. Two people can do anything. And moreover

What do you care if something's abnormal

127

As long as you are normal!

JOHNNY. All right ... if it'll make you any happier ...

HENRY. Wait, wait, stand right here beside me. No one
can see us, right? No one can see us through the key-
hole. This is just between ourselves. Damn it, it's
quiet around here! It's as if there was nothing to it,
but it's enough to give a person the jitters. Sit down.
No, on second thoughts, stand over here, next to this
chair, bow your head

And let your arms droop. Now I'll walk over
To you and stand here beside you and place
My old hand on your young shoulder. It's cold in here!
Chilly, isn't it? I'm touching you ...

MY DEAREST JOHNNY ... No, no, that's quite un-
necessary ... there's no need for any prologue ...
YOU MUST KILL YOURSELF BECAUSE THAT IS MY
WILL. Now answer the way you were told.

JOHNNY. All right. IF THAT IS YOUR WILL , HENRY,
THEN I'D BE GLAD TO.

HENRY. BE PRESENT AT MY WEDDING AND WHEN THE
TIME COMES KILL YOURSELF WITH THIS KNIFE.
(He hands him the knife)

JOHNNY. VERY WELL.

HENRY. Well, what's new Johnny? Tell me, are they
feeding you well at least?

JOHNNY. I can't complain.

HENRY. What time is it?

JOHNNY. Eight-thirty.

HENRY. That watch is worth at least twice the amount you
paid for it - if I remember correctly ...

JOHNNY. I made a good deal on it.

HENRY. It's a good-looking watch. Well, for the time being.
    Good-bye.

JOHNNY. Good-bye. (He exits)

HENRY. (alone)
        A game
        Let's suppose this is a game
        But ... what is it really? To what extent can such
            games be dangerous?
        I would like to know the real capacity of words
        What is my own capacity?
        A dream? Yes, that's right, a dream ... child's
            play ...

(To a piece of furniture) Are you looking at me? I am
caught in a network of glances, in a precinct of looks,
and everything which I am looking at is looking at me

        Even though I'm alone
        Alone
        Surrounded by this silence ... I stick out my arm.
          This ordinary
        Normal
        Commonplace
        Gesture becomes charged with meaning because it's
          not intended
        For anyone in particular ...
        I move my fingers in the silence, and my being
        Expands itself to become itself
        The seed of a seed. I, I, I! I alone!
        And yet if I, I, I alone am, why then
        (Let's try that for effect) am I not?

What does it matter (I ask) that I, I am in the very
middle, the very centre of everything, if I, I can
never be

        Myself?
        I alone.
        I alone.

Now that you're alone, completely alone, you might at
least stop this incessant recitation

This fabrication of words
This production of gestures

But you, even when you're alone, pretend that you're
alone, and you go on

(For once now let's try to be sincere)

Pretending to be yourself
Even to your very self.

I alone
I alone (Let's emphasize that once more) ... while
   out there
Nothing but cries, screams and blood, alas, alas,
   and fear
Oh, never before has any man had
To solve such insoluble problems
Or groan under a more awesome burden
Of pain and dishonour ... How should I view all
   this?

What attitude should I adopt? Why, why,

In the presence of this vile, inhuman
And disgusting world I might wrinkle my brow
And lift my arms to heaven, I might
Roll my hand into a fist or pass my hand
Across my wise and thoughtful brow
I
Yes, that's right, I ... Such are the
Attitudes I might adopt ... in your presence
And for your benefit! But not for my own! I'm not in
   need
Of any attitude! I don't feel
Other people's pain! I only recite
My humanity! No, I do not exist
I haven't any "I", alas, I forge myself
Outside myself, outside myself, alas, alas, oh,
   the hollow

Empty orchestra of my "alas," you rise up from me
  void
And sink back into the void!

Oh, you demagogues!
(Be vehement, sarcastic when you say that)
Whose mouths are full of morality and
Self-righteousness! (Now grimace
Scornfully, mockingly and make a sweeping gesture
  with your hand)
In vain are all your books and philosophies
Articles and lectures,
Systems and arguments,
Definitions and observations,
Visions, revelations and passions before
Before this mass of two billion people
Who are smothering each other in an eternal,
Dark and shapeless, untamed lust ...
In vain does your fly buzz about the nose
Of that green and black abyss (Now let your laugh-
  ter resound
Your private and discreet
Quiet and ineffable
Humanly human laughter ...) While you out there
Persist in your endless posing
We go on pinching ourselves here in our own little
  way
Underneath the bushes of our destiny.

(And now, to bring
This monologue to a close)

I reject every order, every concept
I distrust every abstraction, every doctrine
I don't believe in God or in Reason!
Enough of these gods! Give me man!
May he be like me, troubled and immature
Confused and incomplete, dark and obscure
So I can dance with him! Play with him! Fight with
  him!
Pretend to him! Ingratiate myself with him!
And rape him, love him and forge myself
Anew from him, so I can grow through him, and

in that way
Celebrate my marriage in the sacred human church!

(From all sides enter the DIGNITARIES, LADIES,
CHANCELLOR, CHIEF OF POLICE. Music, ball)

CHORUS.
> The quadrille has begun, let every voice ring!
> Long live His Majesty, His Majesty the King!

HENRY.
> The quadrille has begun, let every voice ring!

CHANCELLOR.
> Long live His Majesty, His Majesty the King!

HENRY. (strolling arm in arm with the CHANCELLOR)
> Look, my good fellow, look how they dance!
> Lulled by the chorus into a wondrous trance
> Oh, the sweet perfume that dreams engender
> Oh, 'tis a night of golden-haired splendour ...

CHANCELLOR.
> This quadrille is stately in the extreme
> It helps to sweeten our every dream
> The soul takes wing, it leaves no tracks
> Its hair is as golden as newly spun flax!

HENRY.
> Though the sense be lacking, let rhyme abound
> The sweet smoke of hopes vain and unsound
> Let rhythm and rhyme spin merrily 'round
> In an unending circle as far as Capetown!

> Pooh! Pooh! Pooh!
> That's enough! Stop!

(The GUESTS stop dancing)

> Tell them to bow!

(They do so)

132

Once more!

(They bow again)

Once more!

(They bow again)

These bows are inflating me ... Where are my men?
(The HENCHMEN come in) I swear they are a fright-
ful lot, amen. Where is the Chief of Police? (CHIEF
comes forward) You and your men are to grab everything and everybody by the snout, amen. If anyone
so much as dares to ... lay a finger on me ... pounce
on him at once. Now then. (Walking among the GUESTS
and scrutinizing them) Is everybody here? That old
battle-axe - who is she?

CHANCELLOR. That's Princess Pirulu.

HENRY. I knew she was a princess the moment I laid
eyes on her - she's so vulgar-looking. And that
moron?

CHANCELLOR. He's a supreme moron.

HENRY. There's a moronic look in his eye. And who's
that flabby, sweaty-looking character with the pot-
belly and the white skin?

CHANCELLOR. A gourmet.

HENRY. He has a pimple behind his ear. What exactly
does he taste?

CHANCELLOR. His own distaste.

HENRY. Good. I see you've brought me the cream of the
crop. (To a HENCHMAN, pointing to the GOURMET)
Step on his foot - but good and hard so it hurts.

(Quiet)

It's quiet here, isn't it? (Glancing around the room)
The very elite, indeed. It's quite evident they re-
present the highest circles of this illustrious king-
dom. But why are they all so old? This is a congress
of old duffers!

CHANCELLOR. I beg your pardon, Sire.

HENRY. But these are not people! These are caricatures!
Just look at all these spectacles, goatees and mous-
taches - how it disgusts me to look at all these shrivelled
up emaciated bodies - these pitiful, sclerotic and des-
pondend varicose veins, fallen arches, sagging
breasts, protruding bellies, false teeth, this inertia,
sclerosis, atrophy, these infirmities and maladies,
defects and blemishes, and all this hideous, shameful
nakedness! And moreover how distinguished they look,
coddled, pampered and fawned upon by the most chic
hairdressers! Hey, corpse, show me your sock:
goodness but that's an exquisite sock, such a tasteful
colour and made of the finest silk too - what an elegant
piece of hose! Only your foot is in a state of decom-
position. These are people already in the process of
disintegrating. They have a cemetery look about them.
And these are the people who govern?

GUESTS. (dancing)
The quadrille has begun, let every voice ring!
Long live His Majesty, His Majesty the King!

(They stop dancing. Enter the LACKEYS with trays
loaded down with bottles)

LACKEYS. Burgundy, Tokay, Malaga, port!

HENRY. (without taking his eyes off the GUESTS) What a
revelry of faces! What a debauchery of noses and
bellies! What an orgy of baldness!

Orchestra of unbridled ugliness
Some music for my wedding! This licentiousness
suits my purpose.

LACKEYS. Burgundy, Tokay, Malaga, port!

HENRY. Where is my fiancee?

CHANCELLOR. Here she comes now with those maidens
dressed all in white.

HENRY. Let her approach and let her smile at me and
lower her eyes as she bows before me. I shall bow
and taking her gently by the shoulders I shall prevent
her from kneeling down, at the same time I shall
smile at her the way I used to do in former times.
(He and MOLLY do so)

CHANCELLOR. (aside) Your Majesty, everyone is
listening.

HENRY. (loudly) That's precisely what I want them to do.
We don't love one another - we merely engender the
feeling of love between us ... (To MOLLY) Why
aren't you smiling? Smile at me, the way you did
before you were raped and became a slut for some
innkeeper, understand? Otherwise, I'll let you have
it. And don't look around - don't try to catch anyone
else's glance - you know I'm jealous of Johnny. (To
the CHANCELLOR) I'm deliberately saying all this
out loud because there's no need to conceal anything
here; here everything is in the open. Look how
graciously she's smiling. That smile evokes within
me a multitude of memories and moves me in the
presence ... in the presence of all these people ...

My darling, if only your smile
Would reverberate off them and come back to me
In waves a hundred times stronger ...
Trust in me, have no fear, I shall find a way
To fill the void of my heart
And I shall love you again, as
I loved you once before.

Let her squeeze my hand in secret. All right. Now
what? What should we do now, Chamberlain, to make
this a truly royal reception?

CHAMBERLAIN. (announces)
        Circle.
        Circle.
        Circle.

LACKEYS. Port!

(The GUESTS group themselves into small circles)

CHAMBERLAIN. With your leave, Sire, with your leave,
    Sire, with your leave, Sire the most illustrious
    names, the greatest fortunes, the highest offices, the
    very flower, the very elite, the very cream, in short,
    You Majesty, everyone - dreams of nothing else save
    the honour to kiss your hand, Sire. I have the honour!
    I have the honour! I have the honour to present to
    His Majesty our renowned poet Paul Valery, the
    undisputed pride and glory of mankind ... and the
    poet Rainer Maria Rilke, likewise the pride and glory
    of mankind. Men of genius! Immortal! Incomparable!

HENRY. Let them pay homage to me. (To MOLLY) Take
    my arm.
    Why are those old ladies bowing to one another and
    not to me? I'm going to blow myself up and squish out
    their guts!

    Who gave any of you permission to clown around?
    There'll be no fooling around in my presence!

CHAMBERLAIN. One moment, Your Majesty, forgive me,
    You Majesty ... Before rendering homage to you,
    they must first of all affirm their own greatness by
    bowing before each other.

HENRY. This one must be having trouble with his kidneys!
    What do you mean they must bow before each other?

CHAMBERLAIN. It's just that the greatness and profundity
    of these two unrivalled poets cannot be fully appre-
    ciated by anybody except themselves. Since all the
    others are lesser poets, they are equally incompetent
    to judge or appreciate or understand them. Therefore

136

by exchanging bows with each other they are testifying
to one another's greatness, which they will then place
at His Majesty's feet.

(The POETS bow before HENRY)

CHANCELLOR. Oh, heaven help us ...

HENRY. Good. The glory of these two melancholy lute
players is now a part of me. Keep on pumping. Who's
that longhaired imbecile over there?

CHAMBERLAIN. A pianist.

HENRY. Why are all those senile old biddies squirming
around over there goggle-eyed, madly clutching their
shrivelled-up breasts?

CHAMBERLAIN. Women always go into convulsions in the
company of an actor, singer, or virtuoso.

HENRY. These are just the sort of second-rate gods I
need. Tell this guy to pump his divinity into me with a
bow. He hasn't got much longer to live anyway - he's
a consumptive. Just look at those delicate fingers.
And this old hag? Why is the scullion arranging a
kneeling rail in front of her?

CHANCELLOR. Oh, heaven help us ...

CHAMBERLAIN. With your leave, Sire ... forgive me,
Sire, it's just that the Princess, as Your Majesty
has already been pleased to remark, is a rather
vulgar woman. She would give anything to fall down
on her knees before Your Majesty, but her knees
are ...

HENRY. (lifting up her skirt) Hm ... as a matter of fact
... she is a little on the dumpy side ...

CHAMBERLAIN. Yes, but she has a servant girl and this
servant girl will render her knees honourable before
they render homage to Your Majesty.

HENRY. To tell you the truth, I would prefer the knees of this young wench.

A LACKEY. (pouring the wine) Burgundy!

CHAMBERLAIN. No, that's impossible! She's this woman's servant.

CHANCELLOR. Her servant. At her service!

HENRY. (to a LADY) What's your name?

LADY. Gertrude.

HENRY. What are you dying from, excuse me, I mean, what are you living on?

LADY. A pension.

HENRY. What do you occupy yourself with?

LADY. My feeble condition.

HENRY. What are you living for?

LADY. To enjoy everybody's respect.

HENRY. This woman is a goddess. An altar adorned with precious jewels and perfumed by the servant girl. Let her kneel down before me on this kneeling rail and let her servant kiss her on the heel. Now start pumping! Oh, how I'm itching! Damn this itching - Chamberlain, scratch me just above my left shoulder blade.

CHAMBERLAIN. Here?

HENRY. No, higher, to the left.

CHAMBERLAIN. Here?

HENRY. No, to the right. Oh, what's the difference. But it annoys me ...

CHAMBERLAIN. (in a confidential manner) It annoys you?

CHANCELLOR. (curious) Does it annoy you?

HENRY. It's nothing, nothing at all. It's even amusing. Where is my father? Show my ex-father in here along with my late mother. We're going to begin right away. (To MOLLY) Squeeze my fingers and I'll squeeze yours ... But the place is so empty. It seems as if there's nobody here.

> I am alone
> Together with you ...

MOLLY. I love you ...

HENRY. That's right, say that, say that out loud so everybody, everybody, everybody can hear. (To the CHANCELLOR) Where is my father? Show that drunkard in too!

CHANCELLOR. (in a perfunctory manner) Your father will be here soon.

HENRY. (in a perfunctory manner) Why isn't my father here?

CHANCELLOR. (as above) He'll be here soon.

HENRY. (as above) If he's going to be here, let him be here.

CHANCELLOR. (as above) Soon it will be that your father will be here.

(The FATHER and MOTHER along with the DRUNKARD are carried in by the HENCHMEN and thrown at Henry's feet)

HENRY. Now what?

CHANCELLOR. Nothing.

CHIEF. Nothing.

HENRY. Nothing.

The same bunch I knelt before a little while ago.

(He nudges his parents with his foot)

I don't know ...
I could eat something ...

FATHER. I could eat something too.

MOTHER. So could I.

HENRY. For the time being though there isn't anything to eat.

MOTHER. Well, if there isn't anything, there isn't anything.

FATHER. Do you remember, Henry, how we used to go for drives in the country together in the wagon?

MOLLY. And I sometimes went along too when the weather was nice.

HENRY. It's true - we had some pleasant outings together ... (He stands up) But that's beside the point. Completely beside the point! This is not the time for chit-chat ... I have to grant myself a marriage!

CHANCELLOR. Grant yourself a marriage!

HENRY. Burgundy!

A LACKEY. Burgundy!

HENRY.
Burgundy!
Hey, Chamberlain, let's empty this goblet
In honour of my lady!

CHAMBERLAIN. Burgundy!

CHANCELLOR. Burgundy!

140

A LACKEY. Burgundy!

HENRY.
>To the health
>Of my loyal subjects!

GUESTS. (raising their goblets)
>Long live His Majesty the King!

LACKEYS. (raising their wine trays)
>Burgundy! Burgundy! Burgundy!

GUESTS. (dancing)
>The quadrille has begun, let every voice ring!
>Long live His Majesty, His Majesty the King!
>Under the spell of this enchanting wine
>May the spell of this ball reach limits sublime!

HENRY. (strolling with MOLLY)
>O 'tis a night of magical splendours
>Illusory is the power that love engenders
>The dreamlike waft of eternal illusions
>And the melancholy music of nostalgic allusions!

MOLLY.
>Oh, the tears I once shed for my maidenly dreams
>A petal adrift on a sea of timid sighs
>The lilacs of the past are in bloom again it seems
>And the brother I feared lost is standing before
>   my eyes.

HENRY.
>Look how gracefully they dance the quadrille!
>It's a dance that's designed to give a man a thrill
>And instruct the human heart in love and good will
>Enough! Enough! Stop!
>(To a LACKEY) Burgundy!

A LACKEY. Burgundy!

HENRY. Burgundy!

A LACKEY. Burgundy!

HENRY. (advancing toward the crowd)
     Get out of my way!
     Move back! I'm advancing
     Toward you! This is my person!
     It is I, I alone! Space!
     Let there be space! It is I who am here!
     Here, in the very centre of everything!
     And now watch carefully!

     Move one of those empty chairs over here, And have
     her sit down on it.
     Now I'll walk up to her and ... and then what? And
     then I'll touch her, for example. I'll touch her with
     this finger ... and that will mean we are married and
     that henceforth she is my legitimate, legal, faithful,
     chaste, and innocent spouse. I don't need any other
     ceremonies. I can invent my own ceremonies. And as
     soon as I touch her, you are to fall down on your knees
     and by the very fact of kneeling down you will elevate
     my touch to the level of a holiness most holy ... to
     the level of a nuptial ceremony ...
     Do you dare not to go down on your knees? Do you
     dare not to consecrate this marriage by kneeling down?
     Now on with it, on with it, come on, let's go, let's go,
     oh Henry, Henry, Henry!

COURT.
     Henry, Henry, Henry!
     On with it! On with it! Oh, Henry, Henry, Henry!

HENRY.
     I don't give a damn
     What any of you may be thinking! But ... what are
       you thinking?
     Do you think that ... that what? (To a LADY) What
       are you thinking?

LADY. I'm not thinking anything.

HENRY. Yes, you are, you're thinking and that goes for
    the rest of you too.

A LACKEY. Port!

CHANCELLOR. They're thinking.

CHIEF. They're thinking ... everyone is thinking ...

HENRY. (thoughtfully) They're thinking ... (He goes from guest to guest, looking each in the face; he bumps into JOHNNY) Oh, Johnny, how are you?

JOHNNY. All right.

HENRY. What's new?

JOHNNY. Not much.

HENRY. Good (They remain standing opposite one another)

CHACELLOR.
His Majesty
Seems curiously absorbed ...

CHIEF.
Yes, the King is absorbed ...

HENRY. (to himself)
I don't want to drink any more ...
I'm not going to drink any more ...
(To everyone)
Are you perhaps thinking
That I am able to rule here solely because
They are shackled ... That I could not
Stand up to them if they were released? ...
(To the CHANCELLOR)
So be it then!
Untie these prisoners and let them attack
Me!

CHANCELLOR. Sire!

CHIEF. Sire!

HENRY. (to JOHNNY)
You know
What's expected of you!
(Aloud)

143

                    Come on! Untie them! Let's make it clear
                    Once and for all who is in command here!

          (The MOTHER and FATHER stand up. Now for the
          first time it is possible to see the frightful state
          this couple is in as their bloody, swollen faces grad-
          ually become visible)

HENRY.
                    What buffoonery!
                    Oh, how frightfully artificial! All the same, this
                       artificiality
                    Is frightful!

CHANCELLOR. They look as though they just got out of
          prison.

HENRY.
                    Are you trying to frighten me?
                    Why don't you go ahead and attack me?
                    Nothing?

CHANCELLOR. Nothing.

CHIEF. Nothing.

DIGNITARY/TRAITOR. Nothing.

          (A group of TRAITORS approaches with evil intentions)

HENRY. Henchmen, get over here!

          (The HENCHMEN come over and stand directly behind
          him)

                    If they attack
                    Me, you attack them ... But
                    Why don't they attack?

CHANCELLOR. Nothing.

CHIEF. Nothing.

DIGNITARY/TRAITOR. Nothing.

CHAMBERLAIN. Nothing.

HENRY.
> I am not ashamed
> I don't feel any pity for you
> Nor am I afraid of you
> No, no ... I merely have to back down from them
> As though I were afraid, as though I were ashamed
>   ...
> I wonder what they're up to.

CHANCELLOR. Nothing.

CHIEF. Nothing.

CHAMBERLAIN. Nothing.

HENRY.
> Ohhh, here they come!
> What do you want? What do you want?

(He runs up to the FATHER, but does not dare touch
him)
> You pig!

DRUNKARD. (violently, off to one side) You pig!

HENRY. (to the DRUNKARD) You pig!

(HENRY and the DRUNKARD come down to the front
of the stage)

DRUNKARD.
> Pig!
> You piggish pigmonger pig of a slut
> Hoggish boar of a greasy porker!

HENRY.
> Sow of a souse!

DRUNKARD.
> Prick of a pig!

145

HENRY.
     Swine!

FATHER.
     Oh, what a pigsty, what a pigsty!

LACKEYS.
     Oh, Burgundy, Burgundy, Burgundy!

DRUNKARD.
     Piggish pig!
     Your girl friend is a slut of a sow! Oink! Oink! Oink!

HENRY.
     You're a pig yourself!
     You pig, pig, pig!

LACKEYS.
     Oh, Burgundy, Burgundy, Burgundy!

HENRY.
     Idiot
     You're an idiot!

DRUNKARD.
     You're the one who's an idiot,
     You idiot! You dried-up tit of a sow!

HENRY.
     Pig puss!

DRUNKARD.
     You're a pig!
     A piggified pig!
     A piggish, piggicized, piggerized superpig!
     Piggy-wiggy! Oink! Oink! Oink!

HENRY.
     Pig!

MOTHER. He's grunting like a hog!

CHIEF. He's drooling like a dog!

146

FATHER. Oh, what swine, oh, what swine!

LACKEYS. Oh, what wine, oh, what wine!

HENRY.
>You boar
>Just try and touch me!

DRUNKARD.
>And I will toushh you
>I'll toushh you yet, I'll toushh you yet
>And then I'll blow myself up and blow this pig down ,
>Squish out his guts and spit all over him! Isn't
>   that right Miss Molly?

>(Quiet)

>Do you see this Finger?

HENRY.
>Say whatever you please
>I'm not afraid ...

DRUNKARD.
>Fellow citizens!

>I ain't no educated man, but I got eyes ... and I see
>they mean to have a pretty posh wedding ... But what
>I keep wonderin' is - how can they go through with
>it, with the wedding I mean, when the bride has
>already been ... ahem ... married to someone else?
>...

>Do you see this Finger?
>Look at my Finger!
>Don't look at anything else but my Finger!

HENRY. But it's tickling me!

DRUNKARD. Don't look at anything else but my Finger!

HENRY.
>I've got goose pimples
>All over me ...

DRUNKARD. Look carefully at my Finger. Look in which
    direction of the room it's pointing ...

HENRY. I feel like laughing ...

DRUNKARD. Look at how my Finger's pointing at some-
    thing over there behind those Personages ... There's
    a young man over there ... Look how I'm pointing
    with my Finger in his direction ... In a second the
    shame of this royal family will be made public ...

HENRY.
        This display
        Is shamelessly
        Touching my Person ...

DRUNKARD. (shouting)
        The King is a cuckold
        His fiancee has been carrying on behind his back!
        Step aside
        And you will see the fellow
        Who's been playing footsie with her!
        There he is, in back of the guests!

(The GUESTS make way, revealing JOHNNY'S CORPSE)

CHANCELLOR. Dead.

CHIEF. Murdered.

FATHER. A corpse.

MOTHER. Dead.

CHAMBERLAIN. A corpse.

DRUNKARD. (startled)
        A corpse!
        I'll be d ... Stabbed with a knife ...
        Who stabbed him?

A GUEST. (to HENRY)
        Sire!

148

He stabbed himself!

DRUNKARD.
> He killed himself? But why?

HENRY.
> On my orders ...

ALL.
> The King, the King!

HENRY.
> But ... is this for real?
> (A moment later)
> Put something under his head.

ALL.
> The King, the King!

HENRY. Who would ever have believed it? It's only a
dream. It's even extremely artificial. And yet he's
lying here

> And she is standing over there
> And here am I.
> (A moment later)
> Now I can grant myself a marriage!

ALL.
> The King, the King, oh, Henry, Henry, Henry!

LACKEYS.
> O Burgundy, Burgundy, Burgundy!

HENRY. Who would have ever believed it? It's nothing
but a dream. The whole thing is even extremely artificial. And yet he's lying there

> And she is standing over there

> (Lowering his voice) I'll walk over to her now and
> make out of her what I damn well please ... I'm going
> to take her and marry her ... with all my power ...

But what was it I wanted to say?

There was something I wanted to say, but now I've
forgotten what it was.
Let's see, what was it? ... Oh, yes! It seems there
isn't going to be any marriage because ...

I don't feel like it any more
(To MOLLY) I'm sorry ...

CHANCELLOR. (upstage, bent over JOHNNY) He's got
bloodstains all over his shirt ...

FATHER. Well, no one can bring him back to life now.

MOTHER. He must have been insane! At first I thought it
was just a joke ... but when I saw the way he was
lying on the ground ...

DRUNKARD. There's no point in talking about it any
more ... He's done for. Finished.

HENRY.
Oh, I know perfectly well it isn't true!
And yet ...
Ladies
And gentlemen
Kneel down and bow your heads
Because instead of a wedding ... there's going to
be a funeral!

CHANCELLOR. A funeral.

FATHER. Well, if there's got to be a funeral, there's got
to be one, I suppose.

HENRY.
Lay him down over here. (To MOLLY) You stand
over here beside him.
This corpse is my creation
But this creation is incomprehensible
Dark
Obscure ...

More powerful than I, and
Perhaps not even my own!
Form a funeral procession!

CHANCELLOR. It's a funeral march!

FATHER. It's a funeral march!

HENRY.
No! I'm not responsible for anything here!
I don't understand my own words!
I have no control over my own deeds!
I know nothing, nothing, nothing, I understand
nothing, nothing, nothing!
Whoever says he understands is a liar!
You don't know anything
Any more than I do!

Being mutually united, we are forever arranging ourselves into new forms
And these forms well up from below. What a peculiar
haze! An inexplicable melody! A delirious dance!
An ambiguous march!

And an earthly human church
Whose priest I am!

DRUNKARD. Whose priest I am ...

FATHER. (tenderly) Henry ...

MOTHER. (tenderly) Henry ...

HENRY.
I am innocent.

I declare that I am as innocent as a child, that I have
done nothing, that I am ignorant of everything ...

No one is responsible for anything here!
There is no such thing as responsiblity!

If however, there is a corpse, then there has to be a

151

funeral, then four of you must stand next to him so
you can raise him up at a signal from me ...

> No, there is no responsibility
> Still, there are formalities
> To be attended to ...

(Four of the DIGNITARIES come over and stand next
to JOHNNY'S CORPSE)

If, however, four of you are standing over there,
next to him, then four of you must stand over here,
next to me.
He and I ... Four and four ... On this side and on
that side ...

MOTHER. My child, don't get yourself all upset, never
mind about all this, Henry darling, I'm your mother
after all. Can't you talk normally any more? Can't
you give me a simple kiss?

HENRY.
> No. Nobody can speak to anybody in a normal
>   manner.
> In vain do you struggle to get free of yourself in
>   order to reach me, and
> In vain do I struggle to get free of myself to reach
>   all of you
>
> Yes, I'm imprisoned ...
>
> I am a prisoner
> Even though I am innocent ... What was it I
>   wanted to say?
> While I am standing here
> And speaking ...
> Let your hands ...
> Touch ... me ...

(The GUARDS who are standing behind him place
their hands on his shoulders)

Wait a minute.
I'm not through yet.

If I am imprisoned here, then somewhere, somewhere
far away, let this deed of mine be raised up on high.

(They lift up JOHNNY'S CORPSE)

And now let this funeral march of yours
Carry you away!

(Procession)

C AND B PLAYSCRIPTS

		Cloth	Paper
* PS 1	TOM PAINE by Paul Foster	21s	6s6d
* PS 2	BALLS and other plays (The Recluse, Hurrah for the Bridge The Hessian Corporal) by Paul Foster	25s	7s6d
PS 3	THREE PLAYS (Lunchtime Concert, Coda The Inhabitants) by Olwen Wymark	21s	6s6d
* PS 4	CLEARWAY by Vivienne C. Welburn	21s	6s6d
* PS 5	JOHNNY SO LONG and THE DRAG by Vivienne C. Welburn	25s	8s6d
* PS 6	SAINT HONEY and OH DAVID, ARE YOU THERE? by Paul Ritchie	25s	10s6d
PS 7	WHY BOURNEMOUTH? and other plays (The Missing Links, An Apple a Day) by John Antrobus	25s	10s0d
* PS 8	THE CARD INDEX and other plays (The Interrupted Act, Gone Out) by Tadeusz Rozewicz trans. Adam Czerniawski	25s	10s6d
PS 9	US by Peter Brook and others	42s	21s0d

		Cloth	Paper
* PS 10	SILENCE and THE LIE by Nathalie Sarraute trans. Maria Jolas	25s	9s0d
* PS 11	THE WITNESSES and other plays (The Old Woman Broods, The Funny Old Man) by Tadeusz Rozewicz trans. Adam Czerniawski	25s	9s0d
* PS 12	THE CENCI by Antonin Artaud trans. Simon Watson-Taylor	18s	7s6d
* PS 13	PRINCESS IVONA by Witold Gombrowicz trans. Krystyna Griffith-Jones and Catherine Robins	21s	8s6d
* PS 14	WIND IN THE BRANCHES OF THE SASSAFRAS by Rene de Obaldia trans. Joseph Foster	25s	9s0d
* PS 15	INSIDE OUT and other plays (Talking of Michaelangelo, Still Fires, Rolley's Grave, Come Tomorrow) by Jan Quackenbush	21s	8s6d
* PS 16	THE SWALLOWS by Roland Dubillard trans. Barbara Wright	25s	9s0d
PS 17	THE DUST OF SUNS by Raymond Roussel trans. Lane Dunlop	25s	9s0d
PS 18	EARLY MORNING by Edward Bond	25s	8s6d

			Cloth	Paper
* PS 40	JAN PALACH by Alan Burns		25s	9s0d
* PS 41	HOUSE OF BONES by Roland Dubillard		25s	9s0d
* PS 42	THE TREADWHEEL and COIL WITHOUT DREAMS by Vivienne C. Welburn		25s	9s0d
PS 43	THE NUNS by Eduardo Manet trans. Robert Baldick		25s	9s0d
PS 44	THE SLEEPERS DEN and OVER GARDENS OUT by Peter Gill		25s	9s0d

* All plays marked thus are represented for dramatic
presentation by:
C and B (Theatre) Ltd, 18 Brewer Street London W1